Awesome African Wildlife

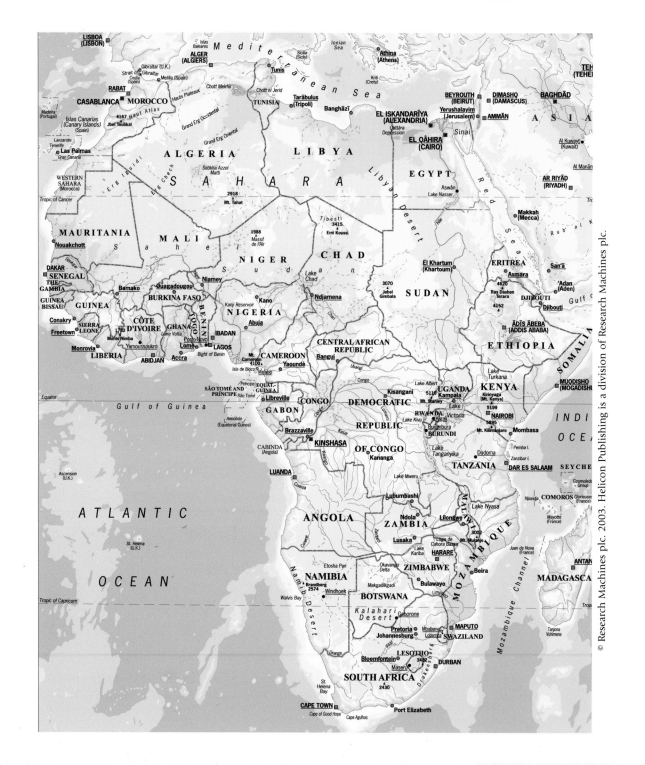

Awesome African Wildlife

Sarah Clark Powdermaker

Illustrations by Pam Carr

PETER E. RANDALL PUBLISHER
2003

Book design by Grace Peirce

Peter E. Randall Publisher
Box 4726, Portsmouth NH 03802
USA
www.PERPublisher.com

ISBN 1-931807-12-4

Library of Congress Control Number: 2003104211

For Mark

CONTENTS

Amazing Sights and Sounds and One Unseen and Silent

Dangerous Dispositions and Defenses

Ancient Animal Symbols, Social Animals, and an Ancient Model of the Highest Social Order

Misleading First Impressions and Fleeting Last Ones

Preface and Acknowledgments

My connections to Africa began at the Washington National Zoo when I was a young child. I loved visiting all the animals, but I developed a particular fondness for snakes and the other reptilians in the reptile house, the ornate brick building that looms in my earliest memories. Another vivid early image is a scene painted on the backdrop of the hippo tank—a broad African river bordered by a green wall of trees—with two shiny, live hippos in the water beneath.

A hands-on reptile experience came in college when my dorm friends and I nursed a baby alligator (we thought) back to health. Its belly had split when it was force-fed too many crumbs of raw hamburger on toothpicks. At the end of the term, as designated guardian, I transported my inches-long ward in a cake tin to the reptile house. The keeper didn't want another 'gator, but when he saw that it was actually an uncommon American crocodile, he accepted it for the collection. Years later I romanticized the incident as my first experience with wildlife preservation, via a tame American, if not a wild African, croc.

My affection for animals and especially for reptiles didn't cause me to become a herpetologist, though I studied zoology and for a while considered becoming a marine biologist. I earned a master's degree in literature instead, became an English teacher, and taught at a California community college. Then I went to Africa. I expected to stay for a year on sabbatical, but I met my husband there, and we stayed for 18 years, living in six East and southern African countries.

This book is another gratifying result of my years of living in Africa and of spending months of time in wildlife parks, especially in Kenya, Zambia, Botswana and Namibia. I intently observed the animals and avidly absorbed information from the guides. I acquired books, subscribed to natural history periodicals, searched the Web, and learned all I could about African wildlife. I'm far from being an expert, but I believe that these 52 articles with their summary verses and original drawings offer an accurate, certainly a heartfelt, picture of the richness of African wildlife.

To make a more orderly book from so much diversity, I gathered the creatures into general groups under informal or whimsical subheadings. They could be arranged in many other ways, just as I could have chosen many other examples, though most of the best-known mammals are here. This is only a sampling, but it has a large goal: to whet readers' interest in learning more about African wildlife so that the wildlife will ultimately benefit. Greater knowledge will lead to greater appreciation of this matchless natural resource, and if it is valued, it will, hopefully, be preserved.

My thanks to everyone in Africa and in America who read the manuscript and gave me thoughtful and constructive comments, particularly Susie and John Latham, Laurie Cameron, Tonya Himmelfarb and Karen Menczer. I am indebted to R. D. Estes for sharing some of his vast knowledge of African wildlife and offering insights and encouragement. My thanks to Pam Carr for her delightful illustrations and to my editors, Helen van Houten and Doris Troy. Any remaining errors of fact or expression are solely my responsibility. Most of all, I am grateful to my husband Mark, who made it all possible.

Amazing Sights and Sounds and One Unseen and Silent

Here a while, then away, Wild Dogs of Africa,
Wide roaming nomads in calico colors,
Pack centered, food sharing, all caring for pups,
And behaving like puppies, they bond with each other.

4

At first scientific glance, the broad, dark muzzle and big ears of the African wild dog suggested it was some kind of hyena, and it was given the name *Hyaena picta*, "painted hyena". But after another look, its pack behavior indicated it was more wolf than hyena, so the name was changed to and remains *Lycaon pictus*, "painted wolflike animal". Its markings have never been an issue: black at the muzzle, white at the tail and mottled in between with daubs and splashes of black, white and yellow or ocher—it looks painted.

Despite appearances, wild dogs are not remotely related to hyenas except that both are carnivores, and DNA tests have shown that they are not descended from wolves. (There is a close relative of the European wolf in Africa—the critically endangered Ethiopian wolf [*Canis simensis*].) Fifteen million years ago wild dogs and wolves had a common ancestor, but the dogs evolved as a separate branch of the canid family tree two to three million years ago. They are one of a kind, an exclusive genus found only in Africa and now found less and less.

Once numerous over much of the continent, wild dogs today are considered vulnerable by the World Conservation Union (IUCN), and many groups are endangered. Populations of a few hundred adults survive only in Botswana, Tanzania and South Africa in packs with an average of ten adults. Small groups live in other countries but in scattered, isolated pockets without safe linking corridors to promote the formation of new packs. (Unusual among social mammals, females emigrate to find mates in other areas while males generally stay in their natal pack.)

Along with the drastic shrinkage of wild land that the dogs need to roam and find mates in, their declining numbers are due to their susceptibility to domestic dogs' diseases and to gunshots. Myths still linger that they attack people (perhaps because of their erroneous connection to European wolves), that they are major killers of livestock, and that they are cruel and wanton predators of wild animals.

The facts are that wild dogs do not attack humans. Like jackals and wolves, they destroy some livestock, but they prefer their natural food of medium-size antelopes, and they often target an unfit member of the herd. When a large pack is hunting, splinter groups may bring down prey, but typically they take only one animal in a cooperative effort that allows them to be on the lookout for trouble while they bolt as much meat as they can as fast as they can.

The dogs kill by disemboweling their prey, which looks cruel and is bloody but can be quicker than killing by suffocation, as cheetahs and leopards do. With the same attack strategy used by spotted hyenas, they bite at their running quarry to cripple it and then tear into it from underneath its body where the hide is thinnest and the vital organs are easiest to reach. The prey, numbed first by adrenaline and then by shock, can be dead in seconds. The dogs need to kill quickly to avoid injury from horns and hooves, but their survival depends on downing the meal before hyenas steal it and before lions try to kill them, their serious competitors for food.

Wild dogs don't fight over food; they rarely fight over anything among themselves. Aggression in the pack is defused by submissiveness in the form of ritual begging, and they use the same puppylike behavior when they greet each other and rally for a hunt. The pups (usually from the alpha female, occasionally from a second female) begin begging adults for meat even before they're weaned, and all the adults regurgitate for them. Wild dogs also regurgitate for an adult that needs food and can't join the hunt—the nursing mother, a baby-sitter that stays at the den, or a wounded dog. Even a very old and decrepit dog is given food by the others. Another exceptional feature of wild dog behavior is that juveniles are always allowed to eat first at the kill, no matter how famished their elders are.

Named for his flying style Bateleur Eagle
Cuts loose with spectacular mating displays.
In his black and white flight suit, red boots and red face mask
He tumbles and loops like a stunt-flying ace.

Like other raptors (diurnal birds of prey as opposed to nocturnal owls), bateleur eagles *(Terathopius ecaudatus)* have a strong, hooked bill for slicing and tearing flesh. They belong to the snake eagle group of eagles because of their bare legs. "True" eagles such as longcrested and tawny eagles have fully feathered legs.

Bateleurs stand out in any crowd of raptors. They have a large head; loose black feathers that give them a rumpled appearance; and bare, bright red legs, feet and face. The distinctive red can be seen even when they fly since their feet stick out beyond their short tail, and they often look down. Their wings are long and white underneath except for a black trailing edge, narrow on females and wide on males. Their tail is so short that it provides little balance, and they rock slightly as they fly, like tightrope acrobats—*bateleurs* in French—tilting their pole as they walk the high wire.

They seldom flap their wings once they're airborne, though they sometimes make a clapping motion. They remain aloft for hours, gliding in widening circles of up to several hundred kilometers. When they perform their impressive mating displays, they dive, twist and loop, and one bateleur was observed coming in for a landing with a full barrel roll onto a limb near his prospective mate. They hunt live prey such as monitor lizards, snakes and small mammals by swooping or by slowly parachuting down with their wings held up and their legs extended. They also feed on carrion, and if they can, they steal food from larger eagles and vultures. Immature bateleurs are sometimes seen along roads scavenging road kills.

Bateleurs are listed as vulnerable in South Africa's *Red Data Book,* which means they will become endangered in the near future if steps are not taken to aid their survival, particularly reducing the use of pesticides and poisoned bait for livestock predators. Their numbers are dropping in settled areas, and they are already gone from large parts of their former range. Other reasons for their decline are their slow maturation and low rate of reproduction.

Like most eagles, a pair of bateleurs raises just one youngster at a time, and the parents continue to feed the fledgling for three or four months after its first flight. The male is especially attentive to his offspring and does most of the feeding during its first days and weeks. But even when it becomes independent, a bateleur isn't fully mature for seven to eight years, the time it needs to go through its rainbow of color changes.

At first its feathers are mottled light brown flecked with white, then dark brown, and then its adult plumage comes in—black and white with chestnut down the back and gray on the shoulders. Its bill is first black, then it becomes permanently blue-gray at the tip and yellow in the middle, fading to red at the base. Its legs and feet are whitish, then purple, then red, and its face goes from greenish blue to purple to orange before it finally turns bright red.

Both immature and adult bateleurs come to drink at waterholes. If there isn't too much activity, they'll hang around for a while, sunbathing with their wings spread, preening their feathers and occasionally catching a glimpse of their reflection in the muddy water.

Startled Impalas like hard rubber balls
Bound in every direction with leaps high and long.
When they're out of harm's way, they re-form in their subgroup:
The stag line or harem or crèche for the young.

Impalas *(Aepyceros melampus)* are some of the most numerous antelopes in East and southern Africa and some of the most handsome. Their bodies are sleek and well proportioned, shiny reddish brown above, tan on the flanks and creamy white underneath. Adult males are somewhat larger than females and have graceful, ridged horns shaped like lyres.

Both sexes and the young, which look like miniature adults, have black-tipped ears, narrow black stripes on and beside their tail and, unique among antelopes, fetlock glands under tufts of black hair on their rear feet. The scent from these glands, which is released when impalas walk or do their high kicks, probably leaves a scent trail in the air for separated animals to follow. They show superficial similarities to several other antelopes, but they have no close relatives. Significant anatomical differences place them in a subfamily all their own (Aepycerotinae).

Partly because of their manageable size (40-70 kg), impalas are a favorite food of several carnivores, and baboons, pythons and martial eagles sometimes take small calves. Yet despite being such good eating to so many, they are thriving in protected areas. One reason for their success is that they're an "edge" species, living both on grasslands and in open woodlands, and they're the first antelopes that return to areas where the grass was burned or overgrazed by livestock. Adaptable in their diet as well as their habitat, they graze on grass during and after the rains, and they browse on the leaves of woody plants and herbs in the dry season.

To reduce the odds of becoming food themselves, impalas respond to immediate danger with erratic behavior. Instead of stampeding in one direction when they're surprised by a predator, they leap high in the air—up to 3 m—or broad-jump up to 12 m, each animal going in a different, unpredictable direction. The explosion of bodies startles the attacker, which can't focus instantly on just one, and the impalas gain a few seconds' head start. Then they regroup and stream off together.

Though not the fastest antelope runners, for short distances they can outrun and outjump most attackers. They sometimes use another tactic when they're pursued by wild dogs: they stand still. Because the dogs hunt by sight, an impala might duck into thick brush and escape by disappearing from view. When a group of impalas is fleeing, one or two stop and stand motionless even in partial view while the dogs race past in pursuit of their conspicuously running and leaping companions.

To detect approaching danger and move away before it comes too close, impalas rely on the collective keen senses of the herd. Group living also lowers an individual's chances of being singled out and brought down. Although predation of newborn and young calves is high, survival odds for each calf are improved by its being born within days or weeks of many others. After a couple of days in hiding, it follows its mother to a nursery group, or crèche, where it stays with the other calves until it is weaned. Then it joins the main herd to become another one of the many.

Klipspringers, "rock jumpers", pairs of dwarf antelopes,
Whistle alarms from steep outcrops and cliffs.
They're fleet and surefooted on the tips of their hooves,
And their hollow fur pads them in case of a slip.

Klipspringers (*Oreotragus oreotragus*) were once hunted so heavily that pockets of populations were exterminated. The reason was their fur, which is unlike any other antelope's. Hollow, coarse and springy (the individual hairs have been described as miniature porcupine quills), it was used to stuff saddles and cushions.

For klipspringers, their fur is both insulation against the temperature extremes of their high elevation habitats and a buffer against sharp rocks and thorns. It's so thick that it makes them look plumper than their 11-12 kg, and it's so loosely attached to their skin that it can help them slip out of a predator's grip. When a klipspringer is seized, its fur comes out in tufts. The unexpected mouthful of prickly hairs momentarily distracts the attacker and gives the klipspringer a chance to escape.

Grayish or yellowish brown depending on the surroundings, klipspringers live in mountainous, rocky habitats from northeast to southwest Africa. They are the only antelopes that can live on the steep hillsides and escarpments and along rocky gorges, so a private buffet of vegetation is theirs for the browsing. Although they prefer to eat leaves, flowers, fruits and seedpods, in the rainy season they sometimes come down to the ground to graze on new grass. They also leave the safety of their rocks when they have to make an often long and always dangerous trek to hunt for a new home. They have been found living on isolated rocky outcrops that are several kilometers away from each other.

Along with their unique coat, their hooves are specialized for the difficult terrain—cylindrical in shape with a hard outer rim and a rubbery inner pad for friction on smooth surfaces. They walk and jump on the tips, like ballet dancers. They can make amazing leaps up slippery cliffs, and when they want to descend quickly, they drop straight onto a narrow ledge, landing on all four hooves, and then onto another, looking as if they're bouncing down the rock face.

Klipspringers are closely related to dik-diks (e.g., *Madoqua kirkii*) and like them they live monogamously in one small territory. (The two species are among less than 5 percent of mammals that live in monogamous pairs, the male mating with the same female through successive breeding seasons and the pair staying together for life.) Klipspringers reproduce about once a year, and the single calf, which weighs little more than a kilo at birth, imme-diately hides and remains hidden for up to three months. This unusually long time for a baby antelope to stay under cover allows it to keep out of sight of cruising eagles while it grows larger and stronger. Its mother returns from browsing to suckle it throughout the day. The male browses less and remains more watchful than his mate so she can eat more and stay in good condition for feeding the baby.

Where there's a constant threat from terrestrial predators like leopards and baboons, the male and female take turns browsing and standing guard. If he detects danger, he stamps his feet and whistles. She whistles in response, and their calls notify the predator that they know it's nearby, so a successful surprise attack won't happen. The whistling duet is also a reinforcement of their pair bond, and it's an audible signal to other klipspringers that the territory is occupied.

The male visually advertises his presence by standing tall on rocks with his four hooves together in the characteristic klipspringer posture. That, along with both sexes' behavior of dashing away and then stopping to look back at a pursuer, once made them easy targets for fur hunters. Today their lingering poses make them easy and photogenic subjects for photographers.

From rain forests down to savannas came Vervets,
The spidery monkeys at ease on the ground.
They're relished by flesh-eaters, furred, winged and scaly,
But saved by troop calls that tell which threat's around.

Cheek-pouched vervets *(Cercopithecus aethiops)*, or savanna monkeys, belong to a genus of colorful-faced, long-legged and long-tailed monkeys called guenons that live in the rain forests of central Africa. Several million years ago their ancestors left the forests for the food-rich savannas. Equipped with their expandable cheek pouches, which can hold as much food as a full stomach, and good sprinting ability for escaping predators, modern vervets have spread in great numbers across the continent.

The faces of vervets are covered in short black fur and surrounded by a headband and sideburns of white fur. But like their forest relatives, they also have colorful features. While most are grizzled brown or gray, some have a green tinge to their fur (and are accordingly called green monkeys). Two unlikely spots of color, concealed when the vervets are relaxed, are their pale pink eyelids. To show aggression to each other and even to humans trying to keep them away from their food, the monkeys thrust out their head, raise their eyebrows, and angrily flash their pink.

More daunting to other vervets is the males' "red, white and blue" display. Males have a bright blue scrotum (sometimes turquoise or powder blue), a red penis, red fur on their anal area, and white fur on their belly, extending above the scrotum. To intimidate a subordinate, a dominant male raises his tail and walks back and forth and sometimes stands directly in front of him. The subordinate, which is usually sitting when the display begins, hunches lower at the spectacular sight and makes appropriately submissive grunts and screams.

Because vervets spend much of their day on the ground, though never far from trees, they're vulnerable to a score of predators. Their eyes are their primary means of defense, and they have keen sight with both color and three-dimensional vision. When a group is foraging, a dominant male sits conspicuously in a nearby tree to keep watch. He also uses the opportunity to keep his dazzling reproductive equipment on view in case another vervet troop enters the territory and wonders if a dominant male is in residence. When he spots danger approaching, he silently leaves his post. The others notice his going or his absence and cautiously move away. He gives an alarm call only if the threat is sudden and close.

If the sentinel or one of the foraging monkeys sees a snake, it "chutters", and the others stand up to locate it and keep their distance. For a leopard the alarm call is a chirp. The others look where the caller is looking and then race for the trees. An eagle alarm call is a low-pitched grunt or bark from the males and a *braup* from females and young. The monkeys look up, come down from treetops if any are foraging or resting there, and then flee into dense brush. (Except in response to aerial predators, vervets go up into trees for safety. Baboons generally come down to be defended on the ground by troop males.) They also respond to the raucous alarm calls of birds like francolins and guinea fowl.

Walking through grass or foraging in it, vervets often pause and use their tail as a prop to stand upright while they scan for trouble. They can run fast, climb trees in a shake and swim well, and they sometimes plunge into water to escape a pursuer. When the lake behind the Kariba Dam in Zimbabwe was filling and trapped animals were being rescued in Operation Noah, vervets would dive underwater down to several meters, trying to elude the persistent predators they had never encountered before—the rescue boats.

The Oxpecker cousins, both Redbilled and Yellowbilled,
Are welcome companions to herbivore hosts.
They relieve them of bloodsucking insects and ticks
And hiss angry warnings when predators approach.

B efore tick dips and sprays, the leading pest-control agents for herbivores, or grazing and browsing animals, were yellowbilled and redbilled oxpeckers (*Buphagus africanus* and *B. erythrorhynchus*). Now with fewer insects to eat on domestic animals and with reduced numbers of wildlife, the oxpeckers, particularly the yellowbills, have also declined in numbers. In many places they are rare or entirely absent.

The birds are still fairly common in large game reserves and in some outlying rural areas. In several countries their ranges overlap, and the two species can be seen on one host. From a distance they look identical because of their same size and dull, buff and brown feathers. Closer up, the redbills can be distinguished by their conspicuous yellow eye rings and solid red bill. The yellowbills have thin eye rings and a thicker yellow bill tipped in red.

The oxpeckers forage on large and medium-size herbivores, five or six birds at a time on a host. Propping themselves like woodpeckers on their stiff tail feathers, they cling to the herbivore's hide with their long claws. They search all over its body, even poking into its nose and ears, for ticks and bloodsucking flies as well as flakes of dead skin and wound tissue. The downside of the servicing is that the yellowbills especially can cause harm by sometimes leaving small sores when they pluck out the pests. (Redbills move their bills like scissors.) More flies are attracted, and the birds continue pecking at them and at the maggots that develop from their eggs, so the wound is slow to heal and may never heal.

But except for elephants, which brush them away with their trunk, the host animals tolerate the jabbing and clawing as well as the sores as a trade-off for the birds' efficient extermination work. The stomach of just one redbilled oxpecker contained the remains of 250 adult ticks and more than 1,000 larval ticks. In return for the endless supply of food, the oxpeckers supply their alertness in spotting danger. Flying off with hissing, cackling alarm calls, they betray approaching predators, human hunters and poachers among them.

Yellowbills like to forage on hippos basking on a bank as well as on grazing Cape buffaloes and warthogs. But of all the herbivores they visit, including domestic livestock, they have a particular preference for giraffes, and they often roost on them at night. The closeness, according to a Bushman legend from southwestern Africa, goes back to ancient times.

When a terrible bushfire was raging across the land, a pair of yellowbills begged Giraffe to lift their nest of newly hatched chicks from a hole in a tall tree trunk. Taking pity on them, he agreed, and after he emerged from the smoke and sparks with the chicks, the overjoyed oxpecker parents asked how they could repay him. Giraffe replied that as he was constantly bothered by ticks and flies, the oxpeckers could ride on him and pick them off, and they gratefully promised to do this forever.

Redbills also like to forage on giraffes, and though they sometimes roost on them, more often they spend the night in nearby trees or reedbeds. The two species build similar nests in the cavities of trees using grass, dung and hairs from the backs of their hosts. The chicks are fed by both parents, and one to three nonbreeding helper birds ply them with additional food. It takes a lot of flies and ticks to satisfy hungry chicks.

Spotted gold Leopard, big cat for all habitats,
Opportunistically eats any meat.
So strong she can haul a fresh kill up a tree
To her storage rack, lookout and daytime retreat.

Although they're not often visible, leopards *(Panthera pardus)* have the widest distribution of all the world's large carnivores, ranging north into Siberia, through the Middle and Far East, and south into South Africa. They continue to be poisoned and trapped in farming areas and illegally hunted in unprotected areas, and small, isolated populations are threatened, but overall the species is not endangered. Adaptation is their main survival strategy. They can live in dense rain forests, on the fringes of deserts, and at elevations up to 4,000 m. The carcass of one leopard that pushed his luck too far was found frozen in ice at 5,600 m on Mount Kilimanjaro. Solitary and secretive, they also live at the edges of many African cities.

Leopards are equally adaptable in their diet: they'll eat almost any animal they come across, dead or alive, freshly dead or in advanced decay. They prefer to hunt living animals about their own size (30-70 kg, depending on habitat), but a single leopard is able to bring down prey as large as a 200 kg kudu. At the other end of the scale, one was observed fishing from an island in a lake. Leopards have a particular taste for meat of the dog family: jackals are among their favorite prey, along with domestic dogs. They also relish baboon meat whenever they can snatch a single animal away from the protection of the watchful and ferocious troop males.

If there are lions or hyenas in the area, a leopard uses its phenomenal strength to hoist its kill up a tree for safekeeping. Holding it by the back of the neck and straddling the body, the leopard slowly jumps and claws up the tree trunk and then onto higher branches. Although the carcass is normally gutted first, it may weigh much more than the leopard, like the very young 100 kg elephant that one leopard wedged in a fork.

With apparent malice, leopards also drape dead competitors in trees. One leopard took up the carcass of a wild dog killed by lions, and others have killed and hung cheetahs in trees. They didn't feed on them, but they have killed and partially eaten other leopards in territorial disputes. When a habitat has few or no trees or competitors, a leopard simply drags the kill into a thicket to eat in the shade.

A leopard's survival skills also include its uncanny ability to keep from being seen. The color of its coat is adapted to blend with the environment, sandy or tawny for deserts and savannas, nearly black for rain forests. Solid dark spots covering its lower body and legs form clusters of rosettes with tan centers on its back. Irregular in size and shape, the spots and rosettes look like patches of sunlight and shade and obscure the smooth, obvious lines of its body. To obscure the telltale roundness of its pale green eyes, a leopard partially lowers its upper eyelids when it is hunting or hiding. Away from thick cover, it spreads itself so flat and stays so motionless even in relatively low grass that it seems to vanish.

On open ground it stalks a meal by creeping from one little patch of cover to another—a small plant or mound of earth—and freezing when the prey looks up. Like most cats it has little stamina for distance running and must get close enough to surprise and seize its victim in a few bounds. Ever the opportunist, on rare occasions a leopard will drop out of a tree onto the back of an animal walking underneath.

DANGEROUS DISPOSITIONS AND DEFENSES

Cantankerous Ratel, the fierce honey badger,
Has jaws like a vise and huge claws sharp as knives.
He'll attack a steel door or a menacing lion
And follow the honeyguide bird to a hive.

34

Like many of its relatives in the Mustelidae family, which includes weasels, zorillas, wolverines and badgers, the honey badger *(Mellivora capensis)*, or *ratel* in Afrikaans, is equipped with formidable defenses. Its skin is extremely tough, thick, and so loose that it sways from side to side as the honey badger moves along in its rolling, pigeon-toed gait. The looseness allows it to twist around and bite any attacker that rashly grasps it by the scruff of the neck, and the thickness helps protect it against bee and scorpion stings and snakebites. Its distinctive fur, jet black on its lower body with a cape of white or silver-gray from forehead to tail, gives a black-white warning that the animal can also produce a foul-smelling secretion from its anal glands.

A honey badger has strong teeth and viselike jaws, and in a fight it may not release its grip until the victim or it is dead. Its huge forepaws and knife-sharp claws are adaptations for digging, and guided by its keen nose, it excavates an assortment of food from dung beetle larvae to mongooses. It also takes the young offspring of large herbivores. It becomes a serious problem when it breaks into pens of small livestock and fowl and then indulges in a frenzy of killing. Quick-tempered and fearless, it goes instantly on the offensive against real and imagined aggressors, even inanimate ones. It will attack a vehicle and tires, and once when a honey badger was caught inside a steel box trap, it ripped its way out, then came back to mangle the trap.

It also mangles other animals. Often cited incidents include a honey badger killing and eating a 3 m python and taking on and seriously injuring a lion before it was finally killed. (A honey badger weighs about 12 kg.) Its most devastating fighting tactic is to tear off the scrotum of a large animal that has somehow provoked it. Honey badgers are known to have removed the scrotum of a wildebeest, a waterbuck and a Cape buffalo, all of which bled to death from the wound. Yet they have been kept as pets by a few intrepid humans, who report that they are very affectionate and intelligent. However, occasionally and with no obvious provocation they go into a brief but furious temper tantrum.

The honey badger gets its Afrikaans name, *ratel,* from the rattling, grating roar it gives as a warning. Its English name refers to its resemblance to badgers, its Northern

Hemisphere counterparts, and to its fondness for honey. Honey badgers as well as humans will follow a honeyguide bird *(Indicator indicator)* to a beehive, guided by the bird's own rattling call, which sounds like a box of wooden matches being shaken. The bird waits for the honey badger to break open the hive for the honey and bee larvae and to expose the beeswax, which the bird craves (and other birds can't digest).

According to accounts in bush lore, before the honey badger rips into a hive it uses its potent anal-sac secretion to fumigate the bees. Backing up to the opening of the hive, it rubs the secretion all around while swirling its tail. The bees that don't fly off are said to die or become immobilized. This fumigation procedure hasn't been witnessed by researchers, but dead bees have been found under and around a hive torn apart by a honey badger, and inside one hive the bees were gathered in a sluggish heap.

The honey badger also uses the overpowering secretion as another of its defenses. But from the same glands it secretes a different, musky-smelling substance for scent marking. The intrepid honey badger owners, though not other people, are often muskily marked by their pets.

The word Hippopotamus means of course river horse:
Hippo is horsy but just in the face.
When he's grazing on land he looks porky, quite harmless,
But he'll take apart anyone crowding his space.

Descended from an ancient piglike ancestor, the hippopotamus (*Hippopotamus amphibius*) is more complex and aggressive than its chubby body and generally lazy manner suggest. A bite from its powerful jaws and tusklike teeth can cut a person in two, and it kills more people than any other wild animal. A small boat and the occupants are attacked if they come too close to a territorial bull or a mother with a calf, and canoes have been splintered by hippos frustrated that they couldn't catch and destroy noisy speedboats. On land a hippo, which can run over 30 kph, will kill to return quickly to the water if a person such as a woman washing clothes appears to be blocking its way.

Hippos leave the water on their rutted paths in early evening to graze, and in the dry season they may walk many kilometers to reach food. (Some hippos just like to walk: one female in South Africa rambled nearly 1,800 km in three years.) They often sleep part of the night on land and return to the water at dawn, spending the day partially submerged because they have no sweat glands and can easily overheat and dehydrate. If they do become overheated, they look as if they're sweating blood when mucous glands in their skin secrete a thick, reddish fluid that hardens to form a protective coating against further sunburn and water loss.

Along with grass, their staple food, hippopotamuses have a taste for agricultural crops, which has caused them to be eradicated from many parts of their former range. Like their omnivorous piglike ancestor and modern pigs, they also eat carrion. They nibble at carcasses floating in the water, and once a hippo was observed chasing crocodiles from a kill to feed on the carcass itself. They also eat fresh meat, occasionally killing for it. One hippo killed and fed on a stranded eland calf, another on a male impala that jumped into its pool.

A remarkable opposite aspect of hippo behavior is their attempts to rescue other animals without eating them, even after they die. Probably the best-known example was filmed in the Kruger National Park in South Africa. A female impala was attacked by a crocodile in a waterhole she had fled into, and as she struggled to keep her head above water, a hippo charged the croc and drove it off. The impala climbed onto the bank but collapsed from exhaustion and loss of blood. The hippo gently lifted her to her feet with its tusks, and the impala staggered a little way but fell again. The hippo felt the impala's wounds with its lips, then tried to raise her head, first with its snout, then with its open jaw. But the impala was dying, and the hippo moved off a few meters and watched until she died. It stayed for some minutes longer and then went back into the water.

Two other hippos attempted to rescue a female kudu that ran into a waterhole to escape a hyena. They herded her to the opposite bank and lifted her onto it with their snouts. She kept jumping back into the security of deep water, but they kept pushing her out until she finally drowned from exhaustion. For more than an hour they tried to lift her body onto the bank, then they left it and went away. And in an uncommon case of aiding their own species (drought-stressed male hippos sometimes kill young males), when a juvenile was trapped by lions near a river, some males emerged, scattered the lions and escorted the youngster back to safety in the water.

Fat, sluggish Puff Adder, drab-colored snake,
Isn't noticed on game trails and paths where he lies.
He inflates, then exhales with a puff before striking:
A person's hurt grossly, an animal dies.

P uff adders *(Bitis arietans)* are responsible for more snakebites and snakebite deaths (mainly in small children) than any other poisonous snake on the continent. They are the most widely distributed poisonous species, and their behavior also puts humans at greater risk of close encounters.

Active at night as well as in cooler parts of the day, puff adders lie motionless in brush, behind rocks or along bare earth paths, waiting for their rodent prey to walk past. Too heavy-bodied to move quickly, they have to rely on immobility and cryptic coloration to catch prey and to avoid danger. Their dull, yellow- or gray-brown bodies are marked with pale stripes and bars that look like dry grass and leaves. Blending inconspicuously into the background, they are easily overlooked by both animals and people who are not expecting to come across them. An unobservant large animal, while not a puff adder menu selection, is struck defensively as it walks past. The snake would much rather put its energy and venom into a rat, mouse or toad.

Puff adders crawl slowly but strike swiftly. They give a brief warning of their intent by expelling inhaled air with a loud hiss or puff. Sometimes they don't follow through with the strike, but when they do, the hissed warning comes too late for most human targets to move out of reach. Through their long (up to 18 mm), front-hinged fangs that fold back into their mouth, they inject a quantity of cytotoxic, tissue-destroying venom into the foot or ankle or into the hand of a person bending down. The bite is instantly and intensely painful and causes a severe wound that takes months to heal. The entire limb and part of the trunk become massively swollen with blood and fluid, and after enormous blisters appear, large areas of overlying skin and tissue die and slough off.

After a puff adder bites a rodent or toad, it withdraws its fangs and the prey staggers off. The snake follows its scent trail, "smelling" with its flicking tongue. It moves caterpillar-like in a straight line as other adders and pythons do; most snakes leave a wavy track. The prey is dead and its cells have begun to break down by the time the puff adder arrives and swallows it head first.

Female puff adders can store viable sperm in their bodies for several years and can produce offspring in subsequent summers without another mating. They give birth to 20 to 50 fully developed young. The babies immediately break out of their transparent, membranous sac, have a short rest, and then crawl off to hide. Only 14 cm long, they're faster moving and more agile than adults, and they're also able to produce and inject venom. It isn't a large amount of venom, but in a world full of predators looking for tender bites, every little bit helps.

Wild cattle of Africa, beefy Cape Buffaloes,
Resemble domestics in movements and form
But meaner—when wounded they turn and fight back,
Goring lions and men with their meat hooks of horns.

46

Africa's hardy wild cattle, Cape buffaloes *(Syncerus caffer)* thrive where domestic cattle can't survive without human intervention. They are resistant to the animal form of sleeping sickness and, with the exception of deadly bovine tuberculosis and rinderpest, to most of the diseases that sicken or kill cattle. Because they can be carriers of some of the diseases themselves, they discourage the expansion of domestic livestock into wild habitats.

Buffaloes eat a wider variety of plants than cattle and many other herbivores because their digestive system breaks down tough cellulose so efficiently. They browse on leaves when grass isn't plentiful, but they graze by preference, eating old and tall grass that most other grazing animals don't like and can't digest. Trampling it as they move through a field, they open up the short grass underneath to animals such as zebras and wildebeests that have more flexible lips for closer cropping.

Like domestic cattle, buffaloes lack water-conserving mechanisms, so they must drink at least once a day, and they also need shade against the midday sun. The herds generally live on well-watered savannas and floodplains with trees or thick brush. They are distantly related to Asian water buffaloes, but their origins in sub-Saharan Africa are unclear.

While they have the same shape and much of the same body language, even the same smell, as domestic cattle, Cape buffaloes are more aggressive and, for security, much quieter. They have several different calls, many similar to cattle calls, but the sounds are lower in pitch and given less frequently. Even when they mass in their immense, dry-season herds of up to several thousand, the noise level is low. At night among trees and brush, their dark, mahogany brown to black coats make them almost as invisible as they are quiet.

Defense of their weakest members and those in difficulty is Cape buffaloes' effective survival strategy. Even blind or crippled animals fare well within the protection of the herd. When lions threaten, the males face them in a line or semicircle with the females and young behind, and old bulls sometimes charge at the mere sight of a predator such as a passing hyena. Once a single lioness that was foolishly stalking and trying to grab a calf was nearly trampled to death when the herd smelled her and charged. Fortunately for her and her cubs, the buffaloes stopped at the edge of a stream as she frantically splashed to safety.

If buffaloes are caught by surprise or unable to identify the danger even though they have approached for a closer look, they usually stampede away. They mob and trample in response to a calf's or an adult's distress call and to an obvious menace like the stalking lioness. Lions that kill a herd member risk injury or death themselves if the herd catches them. Even the lucky ones that escape by climbing trees can be kept treed for several hours by the angry, milling mob.

The herd provides solid protection against lions, the only natural enemy of adults. But away from the main group, a single buffalo, typically an old male, can put up a good solo fight against lions before their combined attack brings it down. Its double-barreled weapon is its huge, outward-curving horns, up to a meter apart from tip to tip. They grow from a heavy base, or boss, and this helmetlike mass of bone is so thick it can stop a bullet. If a buffalo is wounded but not killed by a human hunter, its only other enemy, it will cunningly backtrack and ambush the hunter. Enraged, wounded buffaloes also charge and gore innocent people who happen to be in their line of sight, such as a man walking through a field.

Unthreatened and unharmed, Cape buffaloes are placid, inquisitive and, in one unusual case, protective of an enemy species. An old bull once came to drink at a river where a badly injured man was lying. A hippo had splintered his boat and slashed him, but he had managed to drag himself onto the bank. He was conscious enough to see the buffalo, and he expected that it would finish him off. But after drinking, the buffalo lay down nearby and stayed with the man through the night until he was rescued the next morning.

Zorilla, Striped Polecat, called also *Stinkmuishond*,
Is known for the foul, oily fluid he squirts.
He raises his tail and screams, then fires his weapon
And flops over "dead" if those tactics don't work.

With long, shiny black fur, white stripes down their back, a blaze on their forehead and a white patch on each cheek, zorillas *(Ictonyx striatus)*, or striped polecats, give the unmistakable black-white warning that their major defense is a nauseating anal-sac fluid. A direct hit in the eyes of an attacker can cause blindness because the fluid is so caustic, and its oiliness makes the stench last for days.

A zorilla's first response to danger is to run into the nearest of several refuge holes in its territory. If it is startled or trapped by a predator that disregards its markings, the zorilla allows it one more chance to back off unscathed while erecting the crest of fur on its back and curling and bristling its tail. Then, if the predator still doesn't get the message, the zorilla gives a shrill scream-bark, raises its rear, and turns around to let loose a spray of its foul fluid. As it does, it swings its hindquarters in an arc, ensuring that at least some of the stuff lands on target, since the zorilla can't see clearly over its upended rear end. It can shoot the liquid nearly 2 m.

If the now reeking attacker hasn't been blinded or convinced to look elsewhere for fresh meat, the zorilla falls down and plays dead. Astonished but curious, the predator begins to circle the limp body, which suddenly flips over so that the striped back and anal sac, not the vulnerable belly, are turned toward it. At this point even the most persistent predator has had enough, and as it moves off, the zorilla leaps to life and dashes into a refuge. With such a defense system, these animals are not often taken as prey, but they frequently become road kills because they stand their ground and try to spray approaching vehicles.

Zorillas closely resemble Western Hemisphere skunks, which seem to be properly included in the same Mustelidae family. But DNA tests have found that skunks are so different from other mustelids that they could be given their own family. The identical characteristics of appearance and foul-smell production are examples of convergent evolution—two very distantly related and widely separated groups of animals developing the same successful adaptations.

The white-on-black warning is clearly visible at night when zorillas are active, and their anal-sac secretion is always ready to fire. Therefore they forage noisily, undisturbed by inquisitive predators that come to investigate the sounds. The secretion is also ready to use against their own species even as they display submission. Subordinate animals lower and scrape their forequarters on the ground, but they keep their hindquarters up in case the forward gesture isn't humble enough to prevent aggression.

These little (1-1.5 kg) carnivores don't eat fruits or vegetables, and in very dry areas they don't drink water. They obtain liquids from their mainly insect prey, especially dung beetles and dung beetle larvae, and also from the rodents, reptiles and scorpions they sniff out. Their two or three young, each weighing only 10-15 g, are born blind and hairless with dark stripes faintly visible on their pink skin. But the helpless newborns mature rapidly. They begin catching insects when they're weaned at eight weeks, and by nine weeks they can catch and kill rodents.

Despite their feistiness and intimidating chemical deterrent, zorillas make good pets. They become very tame if they're raised from an early age, and most important, while they may growl or bark in irritation, they don't use their anal-sac secretion against members of the household.

Odd mammals are Pangolins, toothless and furless,
And covered in overlapped, cutting-sharp scales.
When threatened a mother curls tight round her baby,
If handled she saws at the flesh with her tail.

The Cape pangolin *(Manis temminckii)* is one of four species of pangolins in Africa, two terrestrial and two arboreal. Three other species occur in Asia. Its name comes from a Malay word meaning "roller" because rolling into a ball is the key defense of this unique mammal that looks like a reptile.

A pangolin's entire body, except for the underparts and the sides of its thin, pointed face, is covered by grayish brown, overlapping scales that are layered like the leaves of an artichoke. Horny and sharp-edged, the scales are large versions of the same kind of scales that cover the tails of many rodents. They fall out, a few at a time, and new scales replace them. A pangolin's other reptilian characteristic is its apparent lack of hair. But hair is there: a few eyelashes, scattered hairs on its belly, and fluffy, thin hair inside its ear openings. In spite of their similarities, however, pangolins are not remotely related to reptiles, nor are they related to South American armadillos or anteaters, which come from a separate evolutionary line.

A pangolin walks on its hind legs holding its body horizontal to the ground and balancing with its tail. It first freezes when it senses danger, and its dull brown color makes it difficult to see although it's standing erect. Then it tries to move away. But if the attacker overtakes it, the pangolin rolls itself into a ball, tucking its bare face under its tail. On a slope it rolls downhill for a fast getaway; otherwise it stays rolled up and waits to be left alone.

Its long, muscular tail is rounded on top and concave underneath to fit tightly around the pangolin's curled body. If people or a predator such as a lion tries to unroll it, the pangolin slides its tail, still clamped around its body, from side to side, slicing the hands or paws with its scales. A mother curls around a young baby, and to protect an older youngster she covers its head and shoulders while it clasps its tail across hers as she tries to cut the attacker. Finally, a pangolin gives off a particularly foul-smelling secretion from its anal glands to bluff the predator into thinking that its flesh is too foul-tasting to risk getting sliced for.

Also known as the scaly anteater, the pangolin eats almost nothing but ants and termites, and its range is restricted to areas that are populated with a few specific species. It has no teeth, so its stomach grinds up the insects using the sand and gravel swallowed with them. Its tongue, lubricated with sticky saliva, is attached at the rear of its abdominal cavity and is longer than the length of its head and body combined. With loud slurps, the pangolin snakes it into termite holes and then whips it back into its throat pocket covered with insects.

Although they are well armed against natural attackers, many pangolins have been electrocuted trying to climb through electrified game fences. The lethal bottom wire has been removed from some of the fences, but there are further threats from humans, especially to ground-dwelling giant pangolins *(M. gigantea).* This species is listed by the World Conservation Union (IUCN) as rare or vulnerable. In parts of Africa its flesh is a delicacy, and the scales of all four species are valued for their supposed magical powers. The scales of the Asian species are also in demand in China and the Far East for their supposed medicinal properties.

Ancient Animal Symbols, Social Animals, and an Ancient Model of the Highest Social Order

Handsome bird Ibis was once believed Sacred
In black-trimmed white plumage, the head of a god.
These days he's seen commonly feeding in wetlands,
On water birds' breeding grounds, sewage ponds and sod.

The sacred ibis *(Threskiornis aethiopicus)* is one of the most common birds in the continent's moister areas, but since the mid-1800s it has been absent from Egypt, where it acquired its sacred connection. To the ancient Egyptians the ibis represented Thoth, the god of learning and the inventor of speech and writing. In his function as scribe of the gods, he is depicted in a man's body with an ibis head, and he used his reed pen to record the gods' verdict regarding a soul's fate. Any mortal who killed this important symbol was put to death himself.

Sacred ibises are large birds (1.5-2 kg), mostly black and white with a red tinge on their black legs and feet and other red accents in the breeding season. Their bodies are covered with white feathers, their head and neck are bare and black, and they have a very long, downward-curving black bill. When their wings are folded, feathers growing from near their shoulders cover them and their lower back with lacy black plumes. For the breeding season, these feathers grow longer and acquire a purple gloss, and red eye rings appear. But sacred ibises keep their most eye-catching seasonal color concealed until they fly or raise their wings. Then they flash the bright scarlet streaks that have emerged on the bare skin of their underwings.

They're gregarious birds that nest in trees or bushes in colonies of more than 1,000 pairs. The nests are platforms of sticks layered with leaves and grass, and both parents feed their two or three offspring. They fly to and from the nesting sites and feeding grounds in a loose V formation, sometimes croaking as they fly, and they make a variety of calls at the nest.

But their calls are whispers compared with those of their relatives, hadeda (or hadada) ibises *(Bostrychia hagedash)*—large, dark gray or brown birds with horizontal white cheek stripes and metallic green or purple feathers on their wings. Hadedas are named for their calls, among the loudest, most raucous of any bird's *(HAH-de-daa)*. They sound off early in the morning and in the evening. They also call when they leave or return to their nest or perch.

These two ibis species are found across sub-Saharan Africa except in the extreme northeast and southwest, and their ranges overlap in many areas. While hadedas also like moist places, sacred ibises are particularly fond of water sites—inland waterways, wetlands, lakes and lagoons. During the nesting season on offshore islands, they fly out to look for unguarded eggs and chicks. What they eat is as varied as where they live. They're frequently seen feeding at garbage dumps and sewage ponds, and they also eat carrion and swallow dung as they search for dung beetles. Among fresh food favorites are small mammals, reptiles, mollusks and crustaceans.

Hadeda ibises eat much the same fare, though less of the offal and decaying delicacies that sacred ibises relish. Both species use their long, decurved bills to probe for insects and worms along with other buried morsels. Hadeda chicks learn to probe for food early on. During the five weeks they remain in the nest, their parents feed them by simply opening their mouth, and the chicks plunge their head down their throat to share the goulash from the day's foraging.

Dung Beetles do their job cleaning up dung
By eating their fill, making balls of the rest.
When a female crawls onto a male's ball she favors,
With his hind legs he rolls it and her to a nest.

When the ancient Egyptians watched the roller species of dung beetles (family Scarabaeidae) roll and bury dung balls and later saw new life bursting from them, they believed they were seeing the energy and creative force of the sun. These insects became its symbol and were represented in carved likenesses, or scarabs, which gave them their other common name, scarab beetles *(Scarabaeus sacer)*. They came to symbolize both royal power and rebirth into eternal life, and a scarab amulet was placed on the chest of a mummy to stimulate the deceased's rebirth into the next world.

The contributions of dung beetles to this world are enormous. They control flies, destroy the eggs of internal parasites, enrich vegetation by spreading natural fertilizer, increase the soil's porosity by burying dung balls, and pick out seeds in the dung and leave them on the soil's surface, which allows better germination. They and their larvae provide a rich supply of food for many African animals.

There are thousands of species of dung beetles worldwide and about 1,800 in Africa. They come in an array of sizes, shapes and behaviors, and they feed mainly on dung but also on carrion. What they don't eat, most species dispose of either by tunneling under the dung pile and then pushing in chunks as a nest, or by making a ball and rolling it away to a nesting site. The female lays one egg in a ball, and when it hatches, the larva feeds on the dung until it becomes an adult. Some less energetic species just move into the dung pile, and the females lay their eggs inside.

Dung beetles locate a food source by smell, and they fly around over the savanna until they pick up a whiff. Then they gather by the thousands. In Kenya's Tsavo National Park, more than 22,000 beetles were collected from a 7 kg pile of elephant dung in 12 hours. In some species the male and female meet at the dung pile, and when one or both of the pair finish making the ball, they roll it to a nesting site and away from the other beetles that will try to steal it. In other species the male makes a ball, shaping it with his flattened head and forelegs. If a female is impressed with his craftsmanship, she climbs aboard, and he rolls her to a nest with his long hind legs. In the Namib Desert in Namibia dung beetles grab a small pellet from a dung pile, then hold it with their hind legs as they dodge other beetles and scurry away.

Although dung balls are much larger and heavier than the beetles, varying from pea size to the tennis ball size made by the largest nocturnal species, dung beetles seem to have limitless stamina and enthusiasm for their ball rolling. This is explained by a Batonka folktale from Zimbabwe.

In the beginning Dung Beetle, who was a friend of beautiful Butterfly, was dejected that First Man and First Woman always admired his friend and hardly glanced at him. Butterfly told Dung Beetle that he should become strong, as humans admire both beauty and strength. So he exercised hard and became very strong. One day as he was demonstrating his new strength to Butterfly by rolling large balls of dung with his hind legs, the humans walked by. They were filled with admiration, and Dung Beetle was so proud of himself that he has been pushing dung balls ever since.

Bold Black-backed Jackals snatch morsels at lion kills
And rustle young sheep but catch rat and hare pests.
What's rare among mammals, they're mated for life,
And their offspring from one litter help raise the next.

68

Clever, opportunistic and adaptable, the jackal (family Canidae) has featured in African folklore and myths for millennia. In ancient Egypt it was a symbol of death since it was seen coming from the western desert, where the pharaohs' tombs are located, and killing its own prey as well as feeding on carrion. The god Anubis, who oversaw the embalming of bodies and received the mummies into tombs, was depicted as a jackal-headed man.

The particular species in Egyptian mythology was the desert-adapted golden jackal *(Canis aureus)* of northern Africa, which is very similar in social organization and behavior to the black-backed jackal *(C. mesomelas)* of East and southern Africa. Africa's third jackal species, the side-striped *(C. adustus)*, differs from the others in having a less colorful coat and in preferring wooded habitats to open grasslands. The ranges of all three overlap in East Africa.

Black-backed jackals are reddish brown with a black "saddle blanket" on their upper body, wide over the shoulders and neck and tapering to the base of their tail. The black fur is flecked with white or silver-gray, and in East Africa they're also called silver-backed jackals. A Hottentot folktale from South Africa tells how they got this unusual coat. One day the Creator became so angry at Jackal for his endless trickery and thievery that He struck him on the back with a blazing fireball. Jackal managed to put out the flames, but he has never been able to remove the charred black fur with its sprinkling of silvery ashes.

Black-backs are the boldest and most aggressive of the three species, trotting along behind hunting lions and hyenas and then darting in to the kill to snatch scraps of meat. On the coast of Namibia the jackals follow fishermen, wait for them to clean their catch and then feast on the offal. They also come in contact with humans on South African sheep and goat farms, where they kill young animals.

For many decades they have been poisoned, trapped and shot as vermin by the farmers, but instead of being eradicated, the smartest black-backs have become so skillful in avoiding control measures that they are now "super jackals". Because they learn from each other, the young from their mother and one mate from another, they thrive and continue to produce more super jackals. Less cunning black-backs as well as innocent small mammals like aardwolves and bat-eared foxes become victims of the blanket control measures.

Like the other two jackal species, black-backs are omnivorous. Late in the dry season, when many herbivores die from starvation and disease, carrion becomes common food. Otherwise, insects make up half of their diet, and they also eat small animals, birds and wild fruit. They hunt alone or in pairs, but they occasionally take large prey as a group. In Botswana up to 12 were regularly observed attacking old and sick impalas.

Jackals mate for life, and the pairing aids in catching prey such as an antelope calf (one diverts the mother while the other takes the baby) and in defending their territory and raising young. Jackal parents are helped by their grown offspring to bring up the next litter, and the assistance significantly increases the survival of the new pups. But families of black-backs include fewer helpers than those of the other two species. Their youngsters become less sociable as they mature, and the dominant, stronger offspring tend to leave home earlier in favorable conditions. When resources are poor, they force their subordinate siblings out and wait for better days near their parents.

Lionesses work as a team to bring prey down
But feed in a scrimmage of shoving and snapping.
Affectionate, social, except at a carcass,
They groom one another, lie touching while napping.

Except when food is involved, lions *(Panthera leo)* live in a harmonious matriarchal society. The social unit is the pride, composed of between two and forty animals and generally including at least one adult male. Two or more males are often brothers but unrelated to the females, the lionesses, who are close relatives. Young male offspring remain in the pride until their manes develop at about three years, and while they stay, they help the lionesses hunt.

Mature males are well equipped to hunt for themselves, but laid-back pride males let their lionesses do the work. Smaller and less conspicuous without a mane, the lionesses are more successful hunters anyway. They hunt as a group. When one of them decides on a victim, she freezes, then stalks slowly toward it, belly almost on the ground, trying to get as near as possible. With a sprint and a leap, she seizes the animal—usually the closest of a herd, not necessarily the weakest—with one paw across its shoulders or rump, or she jumps on its back. The other lionesses quickly join in, and their combined efforts bring it down. (Cape buffaloes are favorite prey, but a mature male lion's strength is sometimes needed to drop a large bull.) The animal is strangled by one of the lionesses clamping her jaws on its muzzle or biting into its throat, a somewhat slower way of suffocation because of the hard windpipe.

When the hunt is over, the lionesses change personality. Silent and cooperative before, they now snarl, snap and claw as they eat. If the prey is small—a warthog or young antelope—and the pride is hungry, the pride male or males appropriate it, and the lionesses have to wait until they're finished, but the males usually eat the whole thing. Otherwise they all grudgingly feed together, frequently getting up, pushing their way into another place at the carcass, and getting snarled at and cuffed by those already there.

The lionesses' antisocial feeding behavior may be the result of the pride's lack of rank structure. Each female competes more or less equally for meat at a carcass, and when food is scarce, each must fight to get a share before it disappears. A lioness eats on average about 6 kg of meat a day. An adult male can put away more than 40 kg at one time, and within a day or two he can gorge at a new kill, since food passes quickly through a lion's digestive system. Cubs are supposed to eat last, but once when a pride killed a large waterbuck, a six- or seven-month-old cub squeezed under the belly of the male, almost certainly its father, and the two ate together, the cub right under the male's jaws. When there's little food around, cubs may starve. Hungry lionesses always feed themselves first if the males leave anything, and they don't share. Starvation is the main cause of the high mortality among lion cubs, between 50 and 80 percent.

With their bellies full, the lionesses resume their previous sociability and affectionate behavior. They help lick each other clean, rub against and nuzzle each other, and lie down for a nap with their bodies touching. The mothers impartially clean and suckle all the cubs along with their own. Typically the cubs are about the same age, since the lionesses' fertility is synchronized by the brutal reproductive behavior of males.

When a new male or males take over a pride, in order to pass on their genes exclusively, they kill the cubs of the previous males. Despite the risk of being seriously injured or killed themselves, mothers will sometimes attack the newcomers carrying out the infanticide. But when the violent takeover is finished, it's soon forgotten, and the lionesses settle down agreeably with the new males. They go through a long period of mating activity, but the females don't become fertile for several months. Blissfully unaware that the frequent mating is not making babies, the males become bonded to the pride and committed to staying with it. And meanwhile the lionesses' temporary infertility keeps their options open in case bigger and better males come along.

Elephant uses her marvelous trunk
To trumpet, to snorkel, to eat, drink and bathe.
She strokes and caresses to bond with her family
And gives a smart slap if her calf misbehaves.

Depending on the classification system, there are two or three species of modern elephants: the well-known Asian *(Elephas maximus)* and African *(Loxodonta africana)* and the smaller, straight-tusked forest elephant of West Africa *(L. a. cyclotis)*. Along with the extinct mammoth *(Mammuthus)*, these living and dead elephants represent the Elephantidae family, which branched from the Proboscidea order 35 million years ago. Their most ancient proboscidean ancestors, living over 50 million years ago, were small, swamp-dwelling animals that had a flexible upper lip but no proboscis, or trunk.

The trunk was an evolutionary response to the increasing height of early proboscideans. Without a long neck, the animals needed a way of reaching food below and above them, so a proboscis gradually evolved from the fusing of their nose and upper lip. As it got longer, elephants got bigger, since the trunk gave them access to a cornucopia of nutritious food from ground level up to an eventual height of 6 m. By about seven million years ago it had developed the same functions and internal structures, including more than 40,000 muscles, as the trunk of modern elephants. (The trunk's evolution can be seen in an elephant fetus with the initial separation of nose and upper lip and the later combining and lengthening.)

An elephant's trunk is strong enough to uproot young trees, yet with the two fingerlike extensions at the tip (Asian elephants have only one), it can pick up single seeds in the same way the human thumb and forefinger do. The "fingers" are triangular in shape, one above and one below the nostrils, the openings of the nasal tubes that run the length of the trunk. Elephants don't need to look at what they're grasping since their senses of touch and smell are keen, as is their ability to gauge force and distance. One afternoon in Zambia a wild African elephant strolled onto the lawn of a game lodge near the open dining room. A bowl of small round marula fruit, an elephant delicacy, was on a table, and a staff member threw him one. He ate it, and then one at a time she threw out the rest. When she tossed him the last of the pieces, in a this-one's-for-you gesture the elephant fielded it and pitched it back—right into the bowl.

Among its many functions, the trunk figures prominently in giving and receiving information. As a long, extendable nose, it probes the air for smells, and it contains cells that are sensitive to vibrations. By blowing through their nostrils hard enough to make the trunk walls resonate, elephants produce their trademark trumpeting, and depending on the duration and intensity, the sound expresses alarm, warning, a cry for help, and an excited greeting. Being great touchers and feelers, they rub and caress each other with their trunk, and a subordinate elephant puts the tip of its trunk into the mouth of a higher-ranking one, just as an elephant calf does for reassurance. Mothers use their trunk to gently guide and support their infants and to smack an older youngster for bad behavior. Young males test each other's strength by trunk wrestling.

When possible, elephants drink daily, sucking up several liters at a time and then raising their trunk to pour the water down their throat. During a drought a mother will suck water from her stomach and squirt it into the mouth of her baby, and in extreme heat, elephants suck water from their stomach to spray over their back. They draw in sand and dust and spray their bodies to help dislodge ticks when they rub against trees. Spraying soil on their sensitive skin may also be a means of absorbing iodine, the crucial mineral they easily become deficient in.

But their remarkable trunks are not essential for survival. When they have been amputated by crocodiles or poachers' small-game snares, elephants have been seen kneeling down to eat and submerging up to their mouths to drink.

Females head families in Yellow Baboon troops
Protected by powerful, dagger-toothed males.
New black-furred, pink infants first cling to mum's chest,
In a while they ride jockey-style next to her tail.

80

The yellow baboon *(Papio cynocephalus cynocephalus)*, whose range is East and central Africa, is a subspecies of the savanna baboon *(Papio cynocephalus)*. Collectively this species is the continent's most widespread group of primates except for humans. Three other savanna subspecies, the olive *(P. c. anubis)*, the chacma *(P. c. ursinus)*, and the Guinea *(P. c. papio)* of West Africa, are very similar in behavior and appearance to the yellow baboon except that they don't have its brindled, yellow-brown coat and whitish underparts.

Baboon troops are led by males and organized on matrilines. Each kinship group is headed by a female, and all her offspring fit within a strict, age-based order, the youngest ranked first and most important down to the oldest. Young males remain in their mother's group until they grow bigger than the females and develop their canine teeth, which are longer and sharper than lions'. Then, when they're about four years old, they begin moving out to try their reproductive luck in other troops.

One or two immigrants, typically subadults or low-ranking animals, are chosen by a resident female for a lasting and mutually beneficial relationship. She gains an attentive protector for her young, even if they were fathered by others. He gains quicker acceptance into the new troop as well as the chance to father offspring himself when she comes into heat, or estrus.

All baboons are attracted to infants, particularly those still in their black natal coats, and the male friend of a resident female protects her current baby from rowdy juveniles and high-ranking females that try to grab and fondle it. He also protects himself by holding up the infant to counter aggression from dominant males, which will break off an attack at the mere sight of a black-coated baby. The black coat lasts into the third month, when lighter adult fur begins to appear and the baby starts to play with others in its maternity group. The male friend continues to come to its aid when needed, and although he can no longer rely on the solid black fur defense against aggression, the sight of the small baboon normally discourages attack.

Dominant males continually transfer among troops, and they're favored by females to mate with, but the older, more mature males save themselves for females that are most fertile. When females are not in estrus, their sexual skin is flat and black, then it gradually becomes swollen and bright pink as they reach full estrus (about every 36 days). At first they present themselves to several males including subadults, sometimes smacking their lips and seductively raising their eyebrows as they look at them over their shoulders. But it's an offer that young males can refuse. Inexperienced and timid, they give thanks-but-no-thanks responses of polite lip smacking and a quick grooming. Preferring mature, high-ranking mates anyway, the females in full estrus present to and stay near them more than the others.

The most aggressive male is the highest ranking, and he is backed up by other males against predators. When the troop moves toward a dangerous place like high rocks or a waterhole, the males go first as scouts, and they often lead the troop across open areas while other males stay on the flanks and at the rear. High-ranking females, especially those with babies, keep near the center of a moving or foraging group. It's no problem for a leopard to kill a single baboon apart from the troop, but even lions avoid tangling with a platoon of tough male baboons.

Amazing behaviors by little Dwarf Mongooses:
Females join fights with the neighbors for turf,
The males rescue packmates from kidnapping raptors,
And they all gently care for the young and the hurt.

84

Weighing about 300 g, dwarf mongooses *(Helogale parvula)* are the smallest mongooses on the continent, and they're also among the smallest carnivores.

Although most of their diet is made up of insects, on their carnivore menu are small rodents (which they sometimes follow down their burrows), lizards, birds and snakes. Birds' eggs are a rare treat. They can break little ones with their teeth, but they pitch larger ones backward through their hind legs against a rock. Snails and millipedes may also get the same tenderizing treatment.

Unfazed by snakes much bigger than they are, they kill and eat a threatening puff adder or spitting cobra in a group attack led by the alpha female. With their hair-trigger reflexes, they easily avoid its strikes as they dart in to shake the snake by the tail and bite it behind the head until it's dead. They are bold enough to attack a raptor that has seized a pack-mate, and there are several observed cases of successful rescues.

Although they forage as a group, each mongoose goes its own way about 50 m apart, but they stay within earshot of one another's frequent peeping calls. In eastern Kenya foraging dwarf mongoose packs are regularly accompanied by yellowbilled and redbilled hornbills *(Tockus flavirostris* and *T. erythrorhynchus).* The birds hop along with them, eating the same kinds of food they stir up. Because the hornbills sound alarms when they sight a raptor, the mongooses post fewer guards when the birds accompany them. So beneficial to both species is this mutualism that the hungry hornbills will call into the mongooses' current burrow to wake them up if they haven't come out yet.

Their burrows are the ventilation shafts of several termite mounds that they share with the termites, generally spending one night in each. Slow and late starters even with a wake-up call by the hornbills, dwarf mongooses prepare themselves to face the day by sun-bathing, grooming themselves and grooming and scent-marking each other. During these morning activities they're guarded by another mongoose, typically the alpha male. When the alpha female finally leads them off to forage, a juvenile male leaves the group to stand guard nearby for 20 minutes or so until he's relieved. The guarding is a vital part of their life, because their small size makes them vulnerable to a variety of predators, including two other mongoose species.

When the sentinel or one of the foragers sees another pack, which is likely at a territorial border where there's a disputed termite mound, the whole group including the females plunges in for an intense, free-for-all fight. The smaller of the two packs gives way and flees before anyone is badly hurt, but serious injuries occasionally occur. Then the wounded animal or animals are fed, groomed and cuddled for warmth, and the pack forages from the same termite mound until the invalids recover.

Sometimes after these battles a dwarf mongoose, often a juvenile, gets separated and tries to join another group. Or one might emigrate to another pack with fewer animals of its sex so that it will have a better chance to breed. The single immigrant, male or female, is finally accepted after it spends days hanging around, enduring some aggression and behaving submissively.

Once admitted, the new pack member enthusiastically takes on baby-sitting duties. Showing off its nurturing skills, it cares for the young mongooses as though they were its own. This is the main route to becoming one of the only breeding pair, and enterprising immigrants achieve alpha status much more frequently than dwarf mongooses that don't leave home.

Galago, the bushbaby, primitive primate,
Has fingernails, woolly fur, owlish round eyes.
He leaps through dark treetops by light from the stars
And announces his presence with loud bawling cries.

Well known as bushbabies, the little tree-dwelling, nocturnal mammals galagos (family Galagonidae) are prosimians, or lower primates. They're members of one of the two suborders of primates (humans, apes and monkeys make up the other), and like all primates, they have rounded heads and flattened nails instead of claws on their hands and feet.

The nearly 20 species identified so far weigh between 50 g and 2 kg, but their colloquial name bushbaby refers to big sound, not small size. It comes from the raucous distance call of greater, or thick-tailed, bushbabies (e.g., *Otolemur crassicaudatus*). Carrying over long distances at night, the harsh, bawling cry vaguely resembles the wailing of human babies.

Bushbabies have a large repertoire of calls for communicating in dark forests, but even more important to them is olfactory communication. To mark their journeys through the treetops, they leave the scent of their urine on branches by urine-washing, dropping urine into their hands and then rubbing it onto their feet. When they're excited or apprehensive about seeing something new in their environment, they wriggle through drops of urine as they move cautiously to investigate. They also scent-mark their space and one another with secretions from various glands. Both male and female greater bushbabies have a chest gland that secretes a particularly informative substance. Made up of chemicals that evaporate at different rates, the secretion indicates when it was deposited and the age and sex of who did it.

The scents are diffused by bushbabies' fine, woolly fur. They keep it well groomed and in top scent-marking condition with their unusual "tooth comb"—their lower incisor and canine teeth, which have grown together. The comb itself has a special cleaner—a pseudo tongue that lies sandwiched between the floor of their mouth and their real tongue. To groom and scratch areas of their body they can't reach with the comb, they have a grooming claw instead of a nail on a toe of each hind foot.

While galagos can see in bright daylight, their eyes are adapted for seeing in what is total darkness to unspecialized eyes. Behind the retinas of their large, completely round eyes there is a brilliant reflecting layer that gathers the faintest rays of light. In dense forests where only 1 percent of the existing light filters through the vegetation, they can see well enough to make leaps of several meters. Their eyes are immobile in their sockets, but galagos are able to rotate their heads 180 degrees to look directly behind them, and they always check their back before they leap. Smaller and more agile, lesser bushbabies (e.g., *Galago moholi*) make such long and spectacular leaps among thin branches in the darkness that they're also colloquially known as "night apes".

Another adaptation of both species is their batlike ears. In order to hear their insect prey and listen for danger, especially when they venture down from the trees, galagos can move their ears independently, and they can retract and fold them for protection. Lesser bushbabies close their eyes and flatten their ears as they grab rough, stiff-winged grasshoppers and beetles. Once they clasp them securely with their fingers, they bite off the head, then open their eyes and raise their ears. They have opposable thumbs, and they can fold their fingers on their palm, but they can't move them separately, as higher primates do.

Greater bushbabies are heavier and slower than the lesser and other more insectivorous species. They walk along branches like monkeys or hang below the branches and creep along like sloths, slow movements attracting less attention. If they're frightened, they also make long leaps. They come to the ground more than the others, and although the staples of their diet are tree gum and fruit, greater bushbabies have been known to kill chickens and birds as large as guinea fowl. Oddly, they've eaten only the head and neck.

Some Like It Hot and Dry, Others Go Wet

Northeast Africa's underground crowd, Naked Mole-rats,
Are tiny blind rodents in colonies like ants.
They're sausage-shaped, dirty pink, wrinkled and buck-toothed,
And they tunnel like rotors through sunbaked hard land.

T he nineteenth-century naturalists who discovered naked mole-rats *(Heterocephalus glaber)* thought they might have dug up the very young, fetal-looking offspring of larger and hairier adults. (Even now their colloquial name is "sand puppy".) Closer examination of their teeth revealed that these tiny, blind, subterranean animals weighing 30-80 g were fully developed, but developed as what was unclear.

Naked mole-rats are not totally naked: they have some very fine, sparse hair on their body and thicker hair between their toes for sweeping out loose soil when they dig for underground plant parts. They also have hair around their lips to keep soil out of their mouth. They are not moles, which are insectivores, and they are not rats. Scientists eventually determined that the misunderstood and misnamed creatures are rodents but different enough from other rodents to be in a separate family, Bathyergidae, "deep workers".

Their long, curved incisor teeth grow outside their mouth like walrus tusks. These are the tools they use, powered by a quarter of their body's muscle mass in their jaws, to tunnel through compacted soil in search of the roots, bulbs and tubers of desert plants. They dig randomly, and when a mole-rat finds food, it carries a piece to the nest chamber, chirping as it goes, and the smell and chirps send other workers to excavate more.

They work in shifts, the temporary head digger uncovering the food and the others pushing loose soil to the rear for another worker to kick to the surface. The workers shuttle back and forth taking pieces of food to the nest chamber where the huge queen is lying amid a pile of sluggish nonworkers including soldier mole-rats. Like soldier ants and termites, these soldiers will race to any part of the 2- or 3-kilometer-long burrow network to attack a snake intruder, and they can easily kill it with their incisors.

Others in the nest are one or two lethargic males the queen mates with, some nonbreeding females, and the current litter of a dozen or more babies, one of four litters the queen produces a year. She and the babies supplement their fresh vegetables with recycled and processed food in the form of feces that they beg from the nonworkers lying near them. Although this practice is not appetizing to other mammals except rabbits, it allows as much nourishment as possible to be extracted from the food. Serving as living food storage containers may be one of the functions of the nonworkers.

The queen suppresses reproduction in the nonbreeders, including almost all of the workers, with a combination of dominant behavior and pheromones, the chemicals that control physiological and behavioral responses in the same species. The pheromones are produced in her urine, and because all the mole-rats use a communal latrine, they're all exposed to the chemicals. When a queen dies, the other small females grow and become fertile. With their hormones raging, they fight viciously among themselves, and the winner becomes the new queen.

Naked mole-rats are one of only two mammal species in Africa that are eusocial (the other is also a subterranean desert animal, the Damaraland mole-rat [*Cryptomys damarensis*]). For mammals, being eusocial is the same as for bees, termites and ants: division of labor in the community and only one female producing offspring. But whereas the insects come out of their nests for various reasons, naked mole-rats always remain underground. Occasionally a worker's hind feet can be seen pushing loose soil to the surface, but the only other sign of their presence is miniature soil volcanoes.

In scorching hot temperatures ghosty pale Oryxes
Let their own temps soar past 40 degrees.
They're sleek desert antelopes in unisex bodies,
Same black and white markings, same horns like long V's.

The oryx *(Oryx gazella)*, or gemsbok, as it's known in southern Africa, is a gregarious, desert-adapted antelope that belongs to a group called horse antelopes (Hippotragini) because of their stocky, horselike body. Among other species of these "horses" are the jet-black sable *(Hippotragus niger)*, the roan *(H. equinus)*, and the critically endangered addax *(Addax nasomaculatus)* of North Africa. The northern horse antelope *Oryx dammah* may already be extinct in the wild.

Oryx males and females look and act very much alike, and their unisex appearance and behavior arise from living in mixed herds in a difficult desert environment. Because resources are sparse and other oryxes are hard to find, young males especially benefit from remaining in the maternal herd as long as possible to mature. They would be sent packing by the older males if their secondary sex characteristics became obvious and threatening, so except for breeding bulls, oryx males have inconspicuous scrotums. For their unisex role, females have horns, which are longer and sharper though thinner than males', and they're unusually aggressive for female antelopes. Like males, they frequently spar among themselves.

The sexes also resemble each other in their coloration—pale gray or tan with white and black-brown markings on their lower body, legs and face. From the front they have a slightly comical look despite their wicked, V-shaped horns, which first appear as hairy lumps on newborn babies and grow to almost 120 cm. Their round ears stick straight out on small "stalks", and their long white face is partially covered with black-brown patches like greasepaint on a clown.

In older males, distinguishing features are more apparent. Weighing up to 240 kg (females weigh about 210 kg), they have stouter horns, commonly broken from fighting, and thicker necks and shoulders for protection against opponents' horns. While the males' dueling over rank or access to estrous females may result in wounds, fatalities occur mainly when the animals are stressed by drought and famine. Otherwise an oryx fights to kill when it can't escape predators by running.

Cornered, a single oryx can dispatch a single predator, even a lion, but if it's targeted by a group of hyenas, its only hope for survival is backing into a thornbush. Then with its rear protected, it lowers its head so that its horns are horizontal, pointed at the attackers, and swings them from side to side. If the hyenas aren't too hungry, they may decide to look for less challenging prey that has an unprotected rear and shorter horns.

In the vast, arid expanses, oryxes drink whenever water is available. When it isn't, they get the relatively few liters of moisture they need each day (three per 100 kg of weight) by digging up roots and tubers and by eating wild fruit, particularly the tsamma melon and the "gemsbok cucumber". They graze or browse early in the morning after dry grass and vegetation have absorbed airborne moisture through the night—up to 40 percent of the dry weight. Their stomachs contain so much water that Bushmen used them as water sources, straining the liquid through bunches of grass. Oryxes conserve the water already circulating in their body by passing very concentrated, syrupy urine and dry fecal pellets, by not panting open-mouthed, and by not sweating unless they become seriously overheated.

To further control the loss of water in daytime extreme heat and low humidity, they allow their temperature to rise from their normal 35.7 up to 45 degrees. To keep it from going higher until the sun sets and the cool desert night drains away most of the stored heat, they rely on nasal panting.

This adaptation, also used by other dry-habitat animals, is closed-mouth rapid breathing that sweeps air over the nasal mucous membranes. The blood underneath, cooled by evaporation, then flows through a radiator-like network of capillaries surrounding the arteries to the head. The oryx's brain, more sensitive to high heat than its body, is therefore protected by a continual supply of cooled blood until night brings its body temperature down as it plumps up vegetation for next morning's breakfast.

Xeric refers to the driest of habitats
Where creatures adapt to low moisture, scant rainfall.
Some dune-dwelling beetles drink dew in a headstand,
Some gazelles and tall gerenuks don't drink at all.

The word *xeric* applies to a very dry environment—a desert—or to life-forms adapted to living in one. True deserts, defined as areas receiving between 0 and 150 mm of annual rainfall, occur in three places on the continent: the Sahara of North Africa, some of the Horn of Africa in the northeast, and the Namib Desert on the coast of Namibia in the southwest. From a distance these deserts look totally barren, but a few xeric plants manage to grow there, and after a rare rainfall, long-dormant seeds will sprout. In the Namib Desert some small animals and insects have developed ingenious methods for collecting moisture from fog.

The little desert snake, the sidewinding adder *(Bitis peringueyi)*, whose eyes are on top of its head, stretches straight on the surface of sand dunes when fog from the Atlantic Ocean drifts in. Then it moves its mouth back over its scales to suck off the condensation, periodically raising the front of its body to let the water run into its stomach. The web-footed gecko *(Palmatogecko rangei)*, whose webbed feet act like snowshoes on the sand, sticks out its long tongue to lick beads of moisture off its body and the top of its head.

Two species of the Tenebrionidae family of darkling beetles specialize in "fog basking"—standing on their head to let the fog condense on their body and trickle into their mouth. Certain species of *Lepidochora*, the "flying saucer" beetles, plow through the moist surface of the sand, leaving behind them a tiny trench at right angles to the fog-bearing wind. When condensation forms on the slightly raised sides, the beetles suck out the moisture.

Semideserts, which receive an average annual rainfall of 150-300 mm, are also xeric habitats. In these areas, mainly in the northern and southern parts of the continent (tropical rain forests with over 1,500 mm of rainfall occur near the equator in central Africa), the small amounts of rain that do fall tend to be concentrated within one or two months. Consequently life must adjust to drought conditions for at least eight months of the year. Among the most drought-adapted animals are gerenuks *(Litocranius walleri)* of northeastern Africa.

Gerenuks are slender, long-limbed antelopes with a reddish brown saddle and thick, ringed horns that arc back and then hook forward. They can go entirely without drinking, since they conserve water by such means as nasal panting. But it's their access to good food that lets them thrive in conditions difficult even for semidesert animals. They feed on the nutritious small leaves and shoots of shrubs, trees and vines that have a relatively high water content and that last through a drought many weeks after the grass has died. They can browse over 2 m, a level beyond the reach of any antelopes their size (30-50 kg) and beyond most larger ones that keep all four feet on the ground.

What makes the choice buffet available to gerenuks is their unusual ability to feed while standing on their hind legs, resting their front feet lightly on thin branches. Their lumbar vertebrae have modified to allow the curvature of their spine that is necessary to sustain their upright position, and their hind legs and haunches have become strong enough to support their weight. With their exceptionally long neck (they're called *Giraffengazelle* in German), they can reach high and deep into dwarf acacia trees and thornbushes. Their muzzle is small and pointed, and they have large ears with fine sensory hairs and long eyelashes to protect their eyes.

These adaptations for survival in their demanding environment also give gerenuks a graceful, elegant appearance. The ancient Egyptians, admiring their beauty and amazing ability to stand upright, painted their images on the walls of tombs for pharaohs to continue enjoying in the afterlife.

Slim Serval and Swamp Cat like well-watered living,
The five other small cats prefer the dry life.
Serval hunts in high grass, huge ears scanning faint sounds,
And he pounces precisely on marsh rats and mice.

Of Africa's seven small cats only two, the serval *(Felis serval)* and the swamp cat *(F. chaus)*, like living in well-watered habitats and splashing through shallow water to catch frogs and birds. The continent's other small cats—the African wild cat *(F. libyca)*, ancestor of modern cats; the golden cat of West Africa *(F. aurata)*; the lynxlike caracal *(F. caracal)*; the sand cat of the Sahara *(F. margarita)*; and the smallest, at under 2 kg, the black-footed cat *(F. nigripes)*—keep their feet dry in more arid habitats.

The swamp cat is found mainly in Asia, where it's known as the jungle cat. In Africa it has settled into a small niche in the lower Nile valley and lives in marshy areas near cultivated fields. It has pale yellow-brown fur and large black-tufted ears, which it probably uses to locate prey as the serval does. The two are closely related, but the serval's range begins farther south, spreading across the savannas in areas of higher rainfall.

The long legs of these cats and particularly the serval's (which are relatively the longest of any cat's) are adaptations for hunting in tall grass and reeds. The serval also has a very long neck that elevates its huge ears for maximum sound gathering. Active in daylight hours more than most small cats, it hunts well by sight, but it's a specialist in hunting by sound. Its ears are so sensitive that it doesn't hunt in grass during extremely windy conditions because of the background interference.

Moving slowly through high grass, it twists and cups its ears to scan the area for the faintest rustle, preferably from its two favorite prey species, multimammate mice (named for their 12 pairs of nipples) and certain marsh rats. When the serval hears one of these or any of the small animals on its extensive menu, it pinpoints the location so precisely that in one leap it can pounce directly on the prey and kill it with a downward blow from a front foot. It also jumps high to land on an animal with all four feet and then kills it with a bite. Sometimes it tries to flush prey by making a series of high jumps that look as if it's bouncing through the grass.

It pulls down low-flying birds, and with its long forelegs it's able to reach deep into holes and burrows to hook prey. Like the swamp cat, the serval can be seen at night near rural human settlements, attracted by the resident rodents. Once in the neighborhood, a serval will prey on uncaged domestic fowl. It might also reach through the wire mesh of poultry pens to kill and try to pull out a chicken, and numerous large traps with live bait inside have been overturned by eager cats. Because of its habit of returning to the carcass of an animal it has killed (though not to other carrion), it can be trapped itself.

Servals can be dark brown or black in color, and a few are covered in small "freckles", but most are golden-yellow with black spots and bars of combined spots. "Miniature cheetahs", they've been called. An Ndebele folktale from Zimbabwe explains the spots:

In ancient times Serval's coat looked the same as Lion's. Of course he could never be as mighty as Lion, so he longed to be handsome and wear a beautiful spotted coat. One day he came upon Puff Adder, who was very ill. The snake begged the cat for help, for no other animal would come near. Serval felt sorry for him and promised to help if he wouldn't bite, and he agreed.

Puff Adder soon became well under Serval's care and in gratitude offered anything he could give. Serval asked for a spotted coat. The snake said he could provide it, but he would have to bite and inject a little poison. Bravely the cat accepted, recovered from the bite, and then broke out in a rash that left permanent black spots. Serval was delighted with his new coat, and to this day, as a sign of mutual respect, neither animal bothers the other.

Found round the continent Nile Crocodiles
Are the same basic reptiles that thrived in Cretaceous days.
Easy to please crocs eat fishes or fishermen
And hang out by rivers, fresh lakes, brackish bays.

Nile crocodiles *(Crocodylus niloticus)* are found in many African countries that have permanent bodies of water, mainly lakes and rivers but also mangrove swamps and coastal estuaries. Their numbers are greatly reduced in central and West Africa because of overhunting, which once also caused a drastic drop in East and southern African populations. But in several countries Nile crocodiles have made a significant recovery under legal protection. Their future safety is backed up by game ranching, since the skin of this species can be made into high-quality leather.

About 140 million years ago the terrestrial ancestors of modern crocodiles and their relatives became amphibious. The simple but flexible design they evolved for their new aquatic life was so successful that modern animals have changed very little since. They eat whatever flesh comes their way, living or dead, and they tolerate a great range of regional differences as well as changes in their habitat. Thanks to their terrestrial inheritance, in the dry season Nile crocodiles can survive on land well enough to move from one shrinking waterhole or lagoon to another. Fast swimmers, they are unnervingly fast runners, and with their armor of horny plates and their dangerous jaws and tail, predators don't try to slow them down.

Rare among reptiles, crocodile mothers are very protective of their newly hatched young. A female lays about 50 hard-shelled eggs in a hole she digs near a river three to four months before seasonal rains raise the water level, and then she covers the nest with sand. As crocodile breeders know, the sex of the babies is determined during the incubation, females occurring at lower temperatures from eggs at the bottom of the nest and males at higher temperatures near the top, where the sun warms the ground.

For three months the mother goes without eating to stay on or near the nest and guard it from monitor lizards and hyenas, among other predators, including humans. When she hears loud peeping, she uncovers the eggs and the young break out of them with the hard tip on their snout. She then picks up the babies in her mouth, several at a time, and carries them to what seems to be a protected area of shallow water. She continues to guard them for one to several weeks longer, but despite her vigilance, when she leaves to eat or cool off, many of her offspring disappear. Only about 1 percent survive to maturity.

At first the young crocs eat insects and tadpoles, then fish, birds and small mammals. Adults also eat fish, but at their mature length of 3-4 m, they're strong enough to seize a large mammal that comes to drink, erupting out of the water to grab it by the head or leg or sweep it off its feet with their tail. They are a danger to women washing clothes from a riverbank, and they are an occupational hazard for African fishermen. On Lake Victoria fishermen are sometimes seized as they bend over to cast their net or gather it into their boat. If a boat capsizes in the lake or in any crocodile-inhabited water, its occupants probably won't make it back to shore.

Because crocodiles can't chew, they have to swallow small prey whole and eat large prey in chunks. To pull off the chunks, they hold on to the carcass with their jaws and violently twist and spin their body, or they jerk the carcass from side to side until pieces come loose. Sometimes they stash the kill underwater in rocks or submerged trees. This isn't to safeguard or tenderize the meat or to store it for a later meal. They just want to anchor it for easier tearing.

Xenopus, "Peculiar Foot", African Clawed Frog,
Amphibian shaped like a flat wedge of mud:
With his clawed flipper feet he can chase darting minnows
And stir up food lying in stagnant pool sludge.

Amphibians, which include frogs and toads, occupy the rung between fish and reptiles on the evolutionary ladder. The majority are terrestrial, but for a while they all live in the water breathing with gills as tadpoles—their larval stage of development.

In tropical and southern Africa, a widespread group of aquatic frogs and toads is the tongueless Pipidae family, which the African clawed frog *(Xenopus laevis)* belongs to. There are 13 other species in the Xenopus genus, all with webbed back feet and conspicuous black claws on three of the five toes. The claws are used to stir up food in the mud on the bottom of a pool and possibly to create a murky cloud to hide in.

Like all amphibians, African clawed frogs have lungs and breathe air, but they can absorb some oxygen through pores in their skin. A thin film of mucus keeps their skin moist for respiration and slippery for quick movements through the water—darting to the surface for a breath of air or chasing their live prey: water insects, small fish, and tadpoles, including those of their own species. Propelling themselves with their muscular hind legs and large flipper feet, they can swim as fast or faster than most of their prey. In the dry season, if their pool or lagoon dries up, the frogs burrow 25 cm in the mud to estivate until the rains come again. They can remain there for many months, breathing through a small airhole.

Because clawed frogs live in stagnant water with poor visibility (seldom in moving streams), if they can't see food, they find it by smell and by a system of skin receptors called a lateral line, which detects vibrations from movements of other creatures in the water. With their sensitive fingers, four at the end of each foreleg, they also feel for food in the mud and layers of decaying vegetation, picking out tidbits of carrion as well as bottom-dwelling live prey like worms. These "hands" are small and relatively weak, and their forelegs, their "arms", which are joined to their body near the head, are thin and stunted-looking. But when the frogs eat, they move them alternately left and right in arcs that bring their hands directly in position to push food into their mouth.

Both sexes look alike—pale gray-green to muddy or dark brown with pinheads of black eyes set on the top of their head. They have no neck, and their body is flat and triangular, broad at the back and narrow at the front. The male is smaller than the female, but generally they are about 8-12 cm long. The frogs are silent except in the mating season. Then the male makes a soft, underwater buzzing, which he accomplishes without releasing air or making any visible movement. In the brief 24 hours that the female is fertile, she notifies any male in the vicinity with a series of fast clicks like the sound of a Geiger counter near uranium. When the clicking and the buzzing harmonize in a mating embrace, the female deposits her eggs, and the male releases sperm to fertilize them.

Old bald-headed Marabou Stork feeds with vultures
But finds his own frogs, fish and small water things.
He spends his spare time mostly standing around
Or surfing the thermals on his three-meter wings.

Marabou storks *(Leptoptilos crumeniferus)* look their best when they're high in the sky drifting and soaring on their long, charcoal gray wings (3 m wide in East African marabous, 2.5 m in the southern African birds). Once they descend, sometimes with an aerobatic flourish or two, their terrestrial appearance takes a distinct turn for the worse.

They have a huge grayish yellow bill and a faded red, black-mottled head that's bald except for some sparse down feathers. Their neck is dull pink, also thinly covered with down, and from it a fleshy air sac dangles on their breast like an enormous, dirty-pink sausage. Another air sac, orange-red when inflated, lies almost hidden behind their neck at the top of their shoulders. Males inflate both sacs in mating and threat displays, and the festive pink and red balloons not only attract females but also intimidate rivals by their size.

The legs of marabous are black but usually look white because the birds urinate on them to cool them in hot weather, and the dried uric acid remains as powdery white crystals. When they stand still, as they do for much of the day, they draw their head into their shoulders in a deep slouch. (Unlike other storks, they also fly with their head drawn in.) Sometimes they stand on one leg, and sometimes, bending at the tarsal joints, they rest on their long lower legs with their feet sticking straight out in front.

Marabous regularly scavenge at kills alongside vultures, which they can dominate because of their size and their gigantic bill. (They weigh 7-8 kg and stand over 110 cm tall.) But they're basically passive, and they'll give way even to small vultures. Their almost featherless head and neck provide them with the same advantages that improve the quality of life for vultures: they can reach into and withdraw from carcasses more easily and afterward clean their head and neck more thoroughly. In urban areas they gather at garbage dumps and abattoirs, and some locate permanently in towns, where rubbish receptacles are overflowing with a multitude of things to eat. These "town birds" nest in local trees and occasionally stand along roads like slouching, skinny old members of the human community.

Marabous congregate in open areas or on newly plowed fields to switch from scavenging garbage and carrion to foraging for insects. They also gather on sandbanks to wash, rest and do some fishing. If the water is shallow, they wade in and stir it with their feet to find medium-size fish, which they locate by sight and by touch. From the water or the bank they hunt for frogs, snakes and young crocodiles, and they occasionally take immature flamingos. They join the many other predators that converge at the nesting sites of queleas to feast on the newly hatched chicks.

In the mating season, marabous' bare skin turns darker pink and the male, with air sacs inflated, clatters his bill a lot. If he convinces a female that he's the mate for her, she lays two or three eggs in a broad, flat, stick nest, and they take turns brooding for about 30 days. After the young hatch, the parents feed them for another 100 days, until they can fly. When they leave the nest, immature marabous look as if they've come out of a hair salon. In the bloom of youth before they go bald, their heads are covered with a cap of frizzy white down.

Big Appetites,
One Big Guy, and Tricky Little Guys

Queleas are sparrowlike birds by the million,
A storm cloud that swells over grassland and field until
Wheeling and swirling as one they pour down,
And there's not a seed left when they've finished their meal.

In spite of drastic eradication attempts such as dynamiting and a high predation rate for young birds, redbilled queleas *(Quelea quelea)*, pronounced *KWEEL-yas*, survive in hordes across the continent. They are the most numerous birds in the world, and although their numbers vary greatly from year to year and place to place, like swarms of locusts they cause enormous seasonal crop losses.

They feed on standing heads of grain and grass, and they also forage for seeds on the ground, scratching with both feet and then jumping backward to eat. When they mass at waterholes, branches of trees break under their weight and many birds drown. Less destructively to themselves and the trees, a flock drinks by flying low over the surface of the water. The birds at the bottom drop down for a sip, then fly up followed by the next layer, so that the flock looks as if it's rolling over the water.

They fly in the same fast, rolling way, resembling a dense school of small fish constantly changing direction. So synchronized that a flock of tens of thousands moves as one bird, they bank and swirl in alternately light and dark waves, flashing their pale breasts and then their darker brown backs and wing tops. They twitter as they fly, and their wings make a loud, startling whir when they suddenly fly up from foraging on the ground. Back at the nest, queleas vocalize in a metallic chattering, which is deafening close to the colony and sounds like a swarm of bees from a distance.

When the rains come to the savannas after the dry season, the birds rush to breed, and for the occasion the females' bills turn from red to yellow. The males keep their red bills and celebrate the season with a black mask (sometimes white) and a blush of pink or yellow feathers on their head and upper breast. They nest in reedbeds and also in trees, preferably acacias. Each tree may contain up to 500 nests, and a large colony can extend over several hectares.

The male builds the nest by weaving strips of grass into a thin hanging ball like a small purse with a large side opening. Unlike the elaborate nests of their weaver relatives, those of the redbilled queleas are so loosely woven that the two to four pale green eggs can be seen through the strips. Both parents incubate them for about two weeks, though on very hot days they leave the eggs uncovered, and they feed the hatchlings for another 12 days or so.

This is the time of highest mortality for young birds, because many fall from their flimsy nests and are eaten by small carnivorous mammals on the ground. Climbing predators like snakes and monitor lizards crawl up the trees to the nests, and raptors, hornbills and storks fly down to help themselves. Yet the ratio of young birds taken by predators to those that survive remains in balance. Even man has not been able to significantly affect the population.

The eating machines known as Spotted Hyenas
Devour entire carcasses, hide, flesh and bones.
The females get most since they're bigger, more macho,
With pseudo male organs from extra hormones.

128

The hyena family (Hyaenidae) evolved from a branch of carnivores that includes mongooses, civets and genets (the Viverridae), which split from the cat branch. The spotted hyena *(Crocuta crocuta)* is the largest (up to 90 kg) and most common species. The other three are the brown hyena *(Hyaena brunnea)*, the striped hyena *(H. hyaena)*, and the aardwolf *(Proteles cristatus)*.

Along with weeding out unfit prey animals, spotted hyenas clean the habitat of carcasses, even feasting on animals that died of disease including foot-and-mouth and anthrax. They don't become infected themselves, but they have been known to succumb to rabies. Despite their contributions, however, they have little or no redeeming value to most Africans. They sometimes dig up human corpses, and in a few areas they take women and children. They make chilling, humanlike noises, and both sexes appear to have male sex organs. Not surprisingly they're considered vermin and worse—mediums of witches or actual witches themselves.

With the most powerful jaws, teeth and digestive system of any carnivore on land, spotted hyenas are uniquely equipped for their disposal work. They can rip through the toughest hide and crack almost any bone, and they eat and digest virtually every part of a carcass including the teeth and horns. The small percentage of food they don't digest, mainly hair, they disgorge as hair balls. They relish bones, which makes their dried droppings chalky white with calcium and allows females to continue suckling their offspring for over a year.

Notorious scavengers and robbers, they're also efficient hunters. Most spotted hyenas live in a clan, a female-dominated pack, and they hunt as a preorganized group. But often one or two set out independently and are joined by others as they go. When a hunt's not on, they locate kills to scavenge by smell and in daylight by watching for circling vultures. They also listen for other hyenas summoning support against lions or giggling hysterically among themselves, and they listen for the squabbling of lions at a carcass.

One night in Zambia a pride with a subadult, still maneless male killed a Cape buffalo calf. Hyenas gradually approached but hung back shrieking and whooping, trying to frighten the lions away. The lions ignored them, and when the hyenas saw that there was no mature male around—adult males readily kill hyenas—they moved in, nipping at the lionesses' rumps and snatching at the carcass. One hyena grabbed a piece of hide, the young male grabbed the other end, and during the brief tug-of-war the hyena pulled the lion on his belly until he let go. Then the lion "mooned" the hyena, scent-marking and scuffing the ground.

The two competitors despise each other. In an extraordinary event on an Ethiopian desert, lions and hyenas fought a savage running battle every night for two weeks. The lions finally won, although they lost six pride members, when the hyenas gave up after a loss of 35.

With high levels of male hormones (and possible suppression of their own hormone levels by males), spotted hyena females are dominant over males, at least 10 percent larger and much more aggressive. Their bizarre, pseudo male sexual apparatus is a false scrotum made of fatty tissue, a clitoris that becomes as long and erect as a male's penis, and a slit in the glans like the male's urethral opening. The slit widens at maturity and through it, into their fused vagina and urethral duct, they are cautiously and awkwardly inseminated by the highest-ranking male, usually an older immigrant.

They also manage to give birth through the slit to two (sometimes three or four) cubs, which are born well developed and aggressive with their first canine and incisor teeth erupted. If the newborns are the same sex, they immediately begin fighting each other for dominance, and like raptor chicks, the stronger always kills the weaker.

Strength and aggression in female hyenas aren't about territory or mating rights but about food. The best-fed mothers can continue to provide milk to their offspring for up to 15 months. This long-lasting, high-quality nourishment on top of a flood of male hormones further primes their daughters for future dominance and gives their sons a boost toward high rank in other clans.

Elephant Shrews, plainly named for their noses
Like miniature, whiskery elephant trunks,
Are mouse-size insectivores, fur-balls of energy,
Scoffing up insects on round-the-clock hunts.

Elephant shrews were formerly lumped in the order Insectivora along with moles, hedgehogs and the dozens of other African shrew species. But these animals are so different from their relatives that they were later given their own order, Macroscelidea. They live only in Africa and mostly in drier parts of East and southern Africa, yet some are found above the Sahara at the northwest tip of the continent. Ten of the 15 species of elephant shrews belong to the genus *Elephantulus.* They weigh between 25 and 70 g.

Like other shrews they eat insects, mainly ants and termites, but they differ in having pale, soft fur colored by the soil in their habitat; big, keen-sighted eyes surrounded by a white eye ring; and strong hind legs that allow them to jump vertically from a standing position and run with quick leaps and bounds. While all shrews have elongated and flexible snouts, the snouts of elephant shrews look even longer because they're thin and tapered and covered at the base with a cluster of fine whiskers. Glands at the tip secrete substances that may be protection against defense chemicals secreted by soldier ants and termites.

They constantly twitch and wiggle their snout and ears as they scan for food and danger. Rock elephant shrews *(E. myurus)* blend so well into their rocky surroundings that the twitching is the only sign they're not small rocks themselves. Elephant shrews communicate in high-pitched squeaks, and rock elephant shrews add a visual effect, opening their mouth and curling up the tip of their snout like tiny elephants. Another visual display is their territorial posturing—a cakewalk strut on their toes with their fur fluffed out. When alarmed, they make a humming or purring sound by drumming their hind legs on the ground.

Elephant shrews tend to be most active during the day, when some of their main predators, snakes and small raptors, are also active. To reduce their exposure to these and any other predators that happen to be nearby, they dash across open ground from one bit of cover to another. They hunt the same way for their large prey—darting out from behind a rock or shrub to catch a cricket and then darting back with it to their hiding place. They eat small insects, ants and termites wherever they see them and forage for them at dung piles among rocks.

A female elephant shrew becomes sexually mature less than a month and a half after she's born, and her fertility lasts for a year. In that time she can have up to three litters of one or two babies each. They're only 5 cm long, head and body length combined, but for survival they're born well developed and alert. The parents, who jealously chase away trespassers of their own sex, sometimes allow grown offspring to remain in their territory. But there's little overlap of the generations. The entire life span of most *Elephantulus* elephant shrews is about 13 months, though a few species reach a golden old age of 18 months.

Ant Lion larva with large pincer jaws
Is predacious, voracious before he can fly.
He scoops out a sand pit, backs in at the bottom
And waits for trapped insects to grab and suck dry.

As fearsome from an insect's perspective as lions are from a mammal's, ant lion larvae prey ravenously on unwary insects that fall into their trap. Three groups of the vast family Myrmeleontidae are trap builders. The larvae of most of the other species simply lie beneath the surface of the ground waiting for a potential meal to walk or land overhead, but some actively hunt for prey.

An adult winged female deposits about 20 eggs singly in loose soil or sand. Each fat, square-headed larva that hatches excavates a conical pit about 30 mm in diameter by moving backwards in a circular motion under the ground. It digs and flicks away the sandy soil with its head and jaws, or mandibles. Then, with the cone of the pit open at the surface, it backs deeper into the bottom so that only the tips of the long mandibles are sticking out. An ant or other insect that falls in can't climb up the slippery slopes, and to make sure it doesn't come close, the larva pelts it with grains of sand. When the insect finally slides within reach of the mandibles, the larva snatches it and drags it under. A larva takes insects as large as grasshoppers, and if a female ant lion happens to be laying her eggs near sand pits, she too can slip and fall victim to a larva before she can fly out.

Once it pulls its prey underground, the larva sucks out the fluids and pushes aside the dry shell. Its mandibles have teeth for gripping but not for biting, and instead of a mouth it has hollow channels on the insides of the mandibles for the insect's fluids to run through and into its body cavity. The larva also doesn't have an anus, so waste material remains inside until the next molt. While it has to wait to get out of its skin, it can leave a sand pit for a cleaner one whenever it wants. It may dig several new homes during its larval life, coming out at night and relocating nearby.

When it has completed its larval stage, the ant lion spins a cocoon and goes into its intermediary stage as a pupa. Its much less aggressive other self that emerges as an adult looks somewhat similar to a damselfly or dragonfly with its slim body and four gauzy, veined wings. (The wingspan of adult ant lions ranges from 3 mm to more than 160 mm in a species found on Madagascar.) But its body is less colorful, its antennae are thicker, and it is a weaker and clumsier flier.

It forages in the evening and at night, and in the darkness it tries to catch insects that are as slow flying as it is. But around a light, even the fast-fliers become almost as easy to capture as crawling insects trapped in a sand pit. During the day the ant lion rests on the ground or on vegetation, concealed by its transparency. The wings of larger species are mottled like military camouflage uniforms with faint patterns of brown, yellow, black and white.

Forest Hog ranks as the swine family Giant,
Who weighs in at two-sixty kilos or more.
He's tall, dark and hairy with handlebar tusks
And thick cheek pads to head-butt and ram rival boars.

The pig family (Suidae) is represented by six major species in Africa: the giant forest hog *(Hylochoerus meinertzhageni)*, the bushpig *(Potamochoerus larvatus)* and its close relative the red river hog *(P. porcus)* of rain forests, the wild boar of North Africa *(Sus scrofa)*, and two species of warthogs *(Phacochoerus)*. Probably originating in Eurasia, pigs appeared in Africa about 10 million years ago. They arrived in the Western Hemisphere only when humans took them along.

Of all the world's wild species, the giant forest hog is by far the largest: males, or boars, weigh up to 275 kg and stand 1 m at the shoulder (females, or sows, weigh 200 kg or less). Their bodies are covered with long black hair, and their canine teeth grow out and up as tusks over 25 cm long.

They sometimes browse, and they root like other pigs if the ground is soft, but their main food is green grass. Grazing was a late evolutionary adaptation that required the development of strongly anchored muscles on their skull along with other modifications for chewing. These changes also allowed for the development of boars' combat gear: heavily padded, hairless cheeks; a forehead depression made by raised bone and dense tissue; and a broad, thickened snout. They have huge preorbital glands in front of their eyes.

Pairs of young boars begin practicing their fighting skills by pushing each other's snout and trying to land sideward head or body blows. Mature males test each other's strength by pushing with their snout and pressing against each other's forehead. The weaker one eventually turns tail, but if the combatants are evenly matched and neither gives way, the contest escalates into serious aggression. The two boars back off about 25 m and then charge. When they connect, the force can throw one or both of them back on their haunches, and if their hollowed foreheads meet exactly, the compressed air escapes like a rifle shot. Despite the heavy bone and tissue reinforcement, boars' skulls are sometimes fractured in their battles. But underneath the skull is a bony "false hull" that all pigs have, so although their brain is severely jarred by the impacts, it isn't damaged.

They may continue their charging and ramming for half an hour, all the while getting more and more worked up, grinding their teeth and sending out squirts of saliva and urine.

One finally decides he'd rather be grazing and leaves the arena. The victorious gladiator's face is covered with secretions from the preorbital glands, and the smell draws admiring sows for a close sniff. If a confrontation occurs between two family groups, which may include three generations, the young boars sometimes join the fray and spar with each other. When the loser of the two main opponents trots off, the winner's offspring trot along to harass and humiliate him.

Giant forest hogs live in forests in scattered patches across the center of the continent. All populations are listed by the World Conservation Union (IUCN) as rare, and in western areas they are endangered. Not only are their forest habitats being reduced by logging and their grazing areas lost to cultivation, but the hogs are also hunted illegally for their meat for sale in urban markets. They are easily killed by hunters with rifles and dogs because they come to bay to defend themselves.

The adults' chances of survival are much better against their natural enemies, leopards and spotted hyenas, but their piglets are very vulnerable to these and other predators. Both parents fiercely defend them, and boars can kill the predators with their tusks. When a mother leads her piglets out of the forest to graze or when they're threatened in the open, the youngsters walk or cluster beneath her, or try to. Pigs are the only hoofed animals with large multiple births, and giant forest hogs produce from 2 to 11 offspring in each litter. But even one of these big mamas can't shelter all 11 plump piglets beneath her.

Bat-eared Fox looks a rascal, sly smile, mask and all,
But he sticks close to home and helps bring up the cubs.
He's so agile and quick he out-dodges pursuers,
So sharp-eared he hears juicy deep-buried grubs.

Because their fur is so dense, bat-eared foxes *(Otocyon megalotis)* look bigger than their 4-5 kg. When they fluff it up and arch their bushy tail, they look bigger still, a display of size and implied strength to a small predator approaching a den that has young inside. Then the parents chase after the would-be cub-snatcher, snapping and growling and at times giving a high-pitched bark to summon other foxes in the vicinity for a mobbing attack. The illusion of size is enhanced by the black markings that accent their grizzled gray fur—black legs, feet, muzzle and tail, and enormous black-tipped ears. They also have a band of black-brown fur around their eyes like a mask, and their black lips curve upward from their small, pointed muzzle as if they're smiling.

Besides being a size-enhancer, their brush of a tail is a deterrent when they whip it in the face of both terrestrial pursuers and large eagles. It's also a rudder in sharp turns. Even at a fast run, the foxes can reverse direction without losing speed, and they can dodge and zigzag their way out of many chases. Their agility lets them catch fast-moving prey like flying termites or scurrying mice and lizards on the ground. Slower food favorites are scorpions, which they chew briefly and swallow in pieces, stinger and poison sac included. But most of their prey hardly moves at all. Nearly 90 percent of the diet of bat-eared foxes is insects, mainly harvester termites (subfamily Hodotermitinae), which they locate by the sound of crunching when the termites swarm on the surface to cut grass for their underground nest.

The special arrangement of their jaw muscles allows the foxes to open and close their jaws four or five times a second, and their unusually large number of teeth ensures that they can chop hard-bodied insects into tiny pieces. While other canids have only 42 teeth, bat-eared foxes have 46-50, one of the features that place them in a genus all their own, apart from true foxes and jackals, their more carnivorous relatives.

Another insect delicacy is dung beetle larvae, which they also hunt by sound. Their huge oval ears are designed to pick up the faintest stirrings of larvae in burrows or dung balls as deep as 30 cm underground. To locate them, the foxes walk along with their head down, slowly turning it from side to side. When they hear a larva in its dung ball, they bring their ears almost parallel to the ground and rotate them like dish antennae to fix its exact location. Then, even through rock-hard soil, they dig a small trench directly to the grub. Strong diggers with their 2 cm claws, they can easily excavate new dens, but they prefer to do minor interior decoration on abandoned aardvark and springhare burrows.

At large termite swarms where there's plenty of food to go around and individual claims aren't necessary, the foxes feed sociably in family groups. The monogamous, strongly bonded male and female forage together except when they have young cubs. Then the male stays at the den to guard them so the female can eat more to sustain her milk production. Occasionally they share their den with a daughter and her cubs, which are raised communally.

The mates sleep and dust-bathe together and groom and defend each other. The male actively participates in raising the cubs, grooming them, carrying or leading them from one place to another and playing with them. Uncommon for most adult mammals, pairs of bat-eared foxes play together as if they were still youngsters themselves. Adding their specialized quick jumps and dodges to the games, they play-fight, nipping and growling, and chase and tackle each other. If one isn't in the mood and can't be persuaded, the other sometimes plays alone, attacking a tuft of vegetation or tossing a stick in the air.

Meerkats, the mongooses cool in their sunglasses,
Forage by day and take turns standing guard.
Caught short, they bunch bristling and spring up and down
As they head-dart and spit—one weird beast, separate parts.

S un-loving, sociable meerkats *(Suricata suricatta)* sometimes share their underground burrows with two other species, yellow mongooses *(Cynictis penicillata)* and ground squirrels *(Xerus inauris)*. All three parties in the multilevel co-op housing participate in digging new tunnels and entrances and warning of dangerous visitors in the neighborhood, like long-armed servals and long-clawed honey badgers.

Also known as suricates, these mongooses live in close-knit packs of up to 30 in arid areas of southwestern Africa. They have a broad, domed head with low-set, dark ears and relatively small eyes that look large because of the dark fur and skin surrounding them like sunglasses.

Their front claws are adapted for digging into the hard soil for buried insects and larvae, their main prey. They also catch rodents and lizards and will fearlessly take on a big scorpion, first crippling it with sharp nips, then biting off its stinger before eating the body. Although they forage as a group, each one hunts for itself except when there are newly weaned babies to teach. Then an adult caregiver accompanies each youngster, catching food for it and demonstrating how and what to hunt.

Shortly after sunrise, meerkats begin to emerge from their burrow. The first one up stands on its hindlegs to scan for danger, its tail making a third leg like a tripod. At its all-clear call, the others come out and sit or lie on their backs with their sparse belly fur fluffed to expose the skin to the morning rays. When they're warmed up, they're ready to eat, and as they forage or have a midday siesta back at the burrow, they're watched over by one or more sentinels that work in shifts during the day, each animal except pregnant and lactating females taking a turn. Their eyesight is so keen that they can distinguish between an eagle and a harmless vulture when it's only a speck in the sky.

During the sentinel's time on watch, which may last up to an hour, it chirps an all's well every few seconds, which allows the others to forage without constantly checking for predators. But every so often, most of them pause for a quick look anyway. If the sentinel's chirping stops, they are also alerted by the silence. Because meerkats spend most of the daylight hours foraging and because they're small enough (weighing under 1 kg) to be carried off by eagles and hawks, they're vulnerable to aerial as well as terrestrial attack. They have a different alarm call and defense against each.

To warn of a threat from the air, the sentinel gives a shrill, drawn-out call, and they all race for a nearby bolt-hole. If the group is taken by surprise in the open, the adults can only cover the young with their bodies, freeze, and wait for the raptor to disappear. When the danger is a terrestrial predator like a jackal, the sentinel gives short, gruff barks, and the meerkats dive into a nearby hole.

But if they're threatened in the open away from a refuge, their best defense is offense, and they use the same response against rival packs. They bunch together, arch their backs, and with bristling fur, erect tails and lowered heads, they rock and spring up and down, growling, hissing, spitting and darting their heads. They create the effect of a single large and very aggressive alien animal that, for all the jackal knows, could be looking for a meal too.

Slow-fluttering, bright orange butterfly, Joker,
Sports black points and patches like jokers in cards.
His outfit fools birds into thinking he's poisonous
And passing him up for less dangerous marks.

A joker butterfly *(Byblia anvatara acheloia)* would be a treat to eat, but birds rarely do a taste test because its mimicry of the toxic and bad-tasting Acraeidae family of butterflies is so convincing. Most acraeas are red or orange-red with black markings made by the minute, powdery scales that all butterflies and moths have on their wings. The joker is not red but bright orange, a color subtlety that birds don't distinguish, but they do notice its similar black markings, behavior and similar size (4–5 cm).

In typical butterfly fashion, it rests with its wings erect over its body (as opposed to moths, which generally rest with their forewings spread flat over their hind wings). When a joker opens its wings, the mirror-image markings look like an inkblot test. Both its forewings and hind wings have a serrated black border on the outer edges with white specks along the margins, and on the rounded hind wings the border encloses seven orange spots.

A small difference in markings—an additional row of black dots across the middle of each hindwing—distinguishes the joker from its close relative, the common joker *(B. ilithyia)*. The two almost identical butterflies are found together in some areas of southeastern Africa, keeping company with each other, but, because they're separate species, never interbreeding. Like the males of several other butterfly species, male jokers and common jokers sometimes alight on the tops of sunny, rocky outcrops, possibly waiting to be picked up by females cruising for mates.

In further mimicry of the acraeas, the jokers flutter along lackadaisically about a meter or so above the ground. Many poisonous species fly in this tantalizing way, but birds have learned to leave them alone. Nontoxic butterflies tend to fly quickly and erratically to avoid being snapped up.

Moths, the other large group of insects in the Lepidoptera, or "scale-winged" order, avoid predation by flying at night—another difference from butterflies, which are always day-fliers. But the little moths in the Zygaenidae family fly by day, and like jokers, they fly slowly. Their brightly colored scales warn birds that they may be poisonous or at least have a terrible taste. They and their poisonous butterfly cousins acquire the poison in their larval stage as caterpillars, when they feed on poisonous plants. (Lepidopteran caterpillars have chewing mouth-parts that can defoliate entire trees; most adult butterflies and moths feed through a proboscis.)

While butterflies don't gather to dine on milk or freshly churned butter, as people might have believed centuries ago, many species are drawn to flowers. When they alight on a blossom, they uncurl their long proboscis into a straw to suck up the sweet nectar. Practical jokers, to the contrary, feed on such unsavory foods as dung and rotting fruit. But overripe bananas are a fatal delicacy. Butterfly collectors know that the mushy sweet fruit is an irresistible bait to lure both plain jokers and common jokers into their traps.

Since Upupas call *hoop-hoop,* their common name's Hoopoe.
They're black, white and cinnamon, long-billed and crested.
They feed on the ground, and they nest there as well,
But their smell's so repellent they're seldom molested.

156

The hoopoe *(Upupa epops africana)* is conspicuous whatever it's doing—foraging, flying or perching in a tree. Its body and head are the color of cinnamon tinged with pink, and its wings are barred with black and white. Along with this striking coloration, its other distinguishing feature is its large cinnamon crest, black-tipped at the ends of the feathers. When the hoopoe is relaxed, the crest folds into a spike and points backward in a line with its bill. When it's alert or alarmed, it raises the crest and spreads it like a fan. ("Crowned", as in crowned crane or crowned eagle, refers to top feathers that can't be raised and lowered.)

Looking like an animated cartoon character that strayed into a nature film, the hoopoe walks with small, quick steps on its short legs, nodding its head as it goes. It probes the soil for worms and larvae, particularly ant lion larvae, by jabbing its long, thin, slightly down-curved bill into the ground. It also eats frogs and small snakes that it sees as it walks along.

Because its wings are broad and floppy, it flies heavily, rising and dipping like an over-size butterfly. But it's a surprisingly strong flier, and some populations migrate between Africa and Europe and tropical Asia, crossing the Sahara and the Mediterranean. When it flies it looks much whiter than it does on the ground, where its folded wings cover some of the white on its feathers and at the base of its mainly black tail.

Hoopoes sound their mellow, dovelike *hoop-hoop* at the end of the cold season when they're establishing territories and trying to attract a mate. They call from trees since the sounds carry farther from a height. Most birds also avoid calling from the ground because of the risk of drawing attention to themselves from nearby predators, but this is not a concern of hoopoes.

Being tolerant of humans and trusting that humans will tolerate them, they sometimes nest in cavities under the eaves of buildings. But their typical nests are the hole of a tree, a termite mound or an abandoned burrow. They don't do any excavating themselves, and they don't feather their nest or prepare it with grass or twigs. The female lays up to eight pale turquoise eggs with faint white stippling, and she may have two or three broods each season. She does the incubating by herself for about 17 days, and then the male joins in the feeding.

While they're being fed the young birds call *sweet, sweet.* Their unlined nest is anything but. Soon after they hatch, it begins to develop a remarkably foul smell. Adults also have a strong, unpleasant smell and taste, as their black and white markings warn. Therefore hoopoes can nest and forage where they like untroubled by rodents, snakes, or any other predators that come sniffing around.

A whimsical lizard is Flap-necked Chameleon,
Revising his color for background or mood.
He swivels his eyeballs, hangs on by his tail,
And he shoots out his sticky-tipped tongue to nab food.

In a folktale of the Pygmies of the central African rain forests, the First Animal that the Creator made to live on earth was the chameleon (family Chamaeleontidae). Chameleon wandered through the vast forest looking for other animals but sadly found he was alone. One day he heard a soft murmuring coming from a large tree, like the sound of distant birds or running water. He was curious to know what was making the sound, so he struck the trunk with a limb. Water gushed out and spread all around the earth, and with it came all the beasts, birds, fish and insects that now live on the earth. When the water ceased flooding from the tree, a man and a woman appeared. They were the First Pygmies.

Because of its mystifying powers, the chameleon seemed to the Pygmies to be the appropriate agent for bringing animal and human life into the world. Not only can it change color to match its surroundings, it can rotate and focus its bulging eyes independently (an adaptation for sighting insect prey). Since it can look forward and backward at the same time, the Shona people of Zimbabwe believe it can see into the past and the future simultaneously. In a few places these lizards are so feared that they are killed on sight, but in Uganda they are valued for their round, soft-shelled eggs that some people think are good to eat.

A common species in East and southern Africa is flap-necked chameleons (*Chamaeleo dilepsis*), named for the flaps of skin that extend from their head to their shoulders and lie flat until the animals are excited. The wardrobe of other colors they can change into is as varied as their basic body color, which depends on their habitat. Chameleons come in shades of pink to green to brown to almost black, and at night when they're sleeping they look blue-white or yellow in a beam of light. Most have a sprinkling of dark spots on their body, with a pale streak and two pale spots on each side.

When a flap-necked chameleon unrolls its prehensile tail, which it uses as a long extra leg to hold on to branches, its total length is over 30 cm. Its opposing toes allow it to grip with all of its feet or just one at a time. It moves in jerky slow motion among branches and vines, attaching its tail or a back foot to a rear branch while reaching for another in front or below. Its tongue is even longer than its body, and the chameleon keeps it stored inside its mouth until it spots an insect, preferably a grasshopper. Then it shoots out its tongue, captures the insect on the sticky, cupped tip and reels the meal into its mouth.

When chameleons are afraid or angry and especially when the males are trying to intimidate rivals, they put on their elaborate threat display. As their skin goes through rapid color changes, they inflate their body and throat sac, and the bright orange throat skin shows between the scales. They raise the neck flaps behind their head, open their mouth to display the red-orange lining and give a loud hiss. In the heat of confrontation, the males sometimes butt and gum each other. But the special effects are the only weapons these miniature dragons can produce. Harmless even to each other, they have no teeth, claws or venom.

Gray-like-bark Vine Snake can see three-dimensionally
Spotting and stalking his tree lizard prey.
He's disguised as a branch and he packs potent venom,
Yet often when threatened he just glides away.

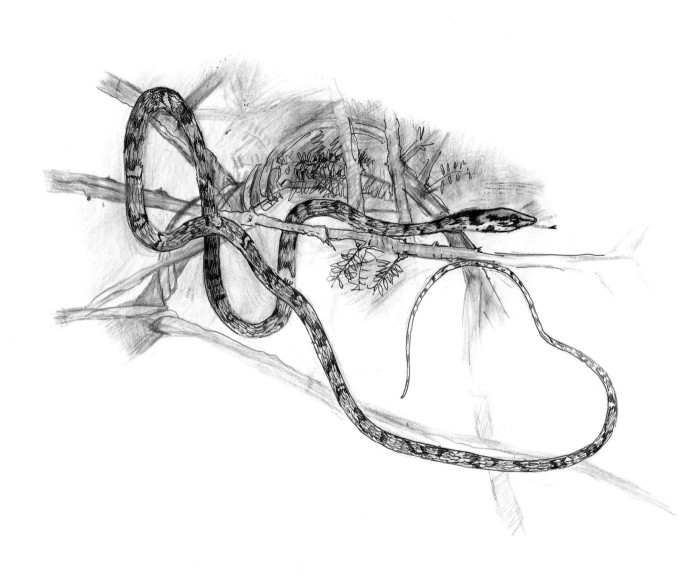

164

The tree-dwelling vine snake *(Thelotornis capensis)* is also called the twig snake because it mimics the appearance and motions of both these plant parts. A short (1 m), thin snake, its skin is mottled gray with black flecks and pale streaks like bark, and the top of its long, pointed head is leaf green. When it's resting or lying on a branch waiting for a meal to appear nearby, its camouflage is so realistic that it looks like a twig with a leaf on top.

When it stalks prey, an arboreal lizard such as a chameleon, a tree frog, another snake or a fledgling bird, it moves so slowly that the branch seems to be growing by the millimeter. It does its vine mimicry with its odd behavior of extending the front third of its body from the foliage and remaining in this position for many minutes. When a breeze stirs the branches, the snake sways in unison like a vine.

It has the unusual ability to see in depth in a reptilian kind of three-dimensional, or binocular, vision. This is made possible by its peculiar horizontal pupils shaped like old-fashioned keyholes and by an indentation running from eyes to snout. Without a bony ridge in between, as other snakes have, its eyes can focus together. Once it spots prey, which may be both motionless and well camouflaged, the snake glides closer until it is within striking range, then seizes the victim by the nape of the neck. If the prey is able to move out of range in time, the snake will continue stalking it.

The vine snake is back fanged; its fangs are short and lie below its eyes rather than at the front of its mouth. Consequently, it has to work its jaws in steplike movements for the fangs to penetrate a victim's flesh and inject venom. The process often causes the prey to slip off the branch, and the snake finishes its meal hanging head down and swallowing upward.

Like most snakes, the vine snake's first and most usual response to an approaching animal is to glide quickly off. But if it stays and displays, it inflates its throat and flicks its two-toned tongue, black at the tip and bright orange at the back. If it finally decides to strike, it seems to do so halfheartedly, and its aim is often inaccurate as though striking at a predator isn't worth as much effort as striking at a potential meal. Also, because the snake's fangs are at the back of its mouth, it cannot easily sink them into the flesh of large animals, so human bodies are rarely bitten, though their hands and fingers are vulnerable.

Most back-fanged snakes are only moderately poisonous, but the vine snake is one of two in southern Africa whose bite can be fatal to man. The other snake is the boomslang *(Dispholidus typus)*. The venom of these two contains a hemotoxin, a type of poison that disrupts the clotting of blood and causes massive hemorrhaging. Antivenin exists for boomslang bites, but it is useless against vine snake venom. The rare human victim can be treated only by a complete blood transfusion.

NOW WE SEE THEM . . .

Africa's horses of different stripes, Zebras,
Are white, stenciled black, from their tail through their mane.
The stripes help conceal them among other stripes,
But they're ID to zebras—no two look the same.

Out of North America came the first horses, the "dawn horses", and their descendants entered Africa over ancient land bridges two to three million years ago. These new-comers, the ancestors of zebras and wild asses, were able to compete successfully with the native herbivores because of their ability to eat and rapidly digest tough grasses. They are now represented in Africa by four species: the widespread plains, or Burchell's, zebra *(Equus burchelli)*, which has brown "shadow" stripes between its black stripes; the mountain zebra *(E. zebra)*; Grevy's zebra *(E. grevyi)*; and the wild ass *(E. africanus)*, the ancestor of domestic donkeys. All these animals are completely or partially striped and have a large, long head, stocky body, short mane and a single toe inside each hoof.

The bold black-on-white stripes of zebras are not a warning of bad taste and smell—zebras are a favorite food of lions—but a means of making themselves less conspicuous to predators and also of identifying themselves to other zebras. On the open plains in shimmering, midday heat as well as in dim light, the stripes create a wavy gray screen. When zebras drink shoulder to shoulder at a waterhole or bunch to flee from danger, the stripes obscure the outlines of each individual body so that a predator has a harder time singling one out.

To members of the herd the stripes present instant identification, since no two patterns are the same, and zebras are highly sensitive to individual variations. They are also visually stimulated by black and white stripes, and they are attracted to them on other zebras as well as to stripes painted on experimental panels. One of the first lessons for a newborn foal is to learn its mother's stripe pattern. For several days after its birth she keeps herself between the foal and other herd members so that it will imprint only on her stripes.

According to a Zulu folktale from South Africa, zebras' stripes are their ribbons of courage. Long ago a fierce baboon came to live beside the Umfolozi River. He declared that the river now belonged to him and the other animals could not drink from it. A young zebra stallion, who was pure white as zebras used to be, challenged the baboon to a fight for the water. After a long struggle, Baboon threw Zebra on his back over blazing logs in a fire. But instead of defeating him, the terrible pain renewed Zebra's strength. He kicked

Baboon so hard that the monkey went sailing over the river onto some distant rocks and landed with such force on his rear that it is bald to this day. Zebra also bears marks of the battle on his once pure white coat, but the water remains free to all who live on the broad plains, and Baboon still lives among the rocks.

Some zebras wear additional battle ribbons: long scars on their rump and flanks from the claws of lions that couldn't bring them down. Like domestic horses, both males and females bite and kick hard. They can kill a hyena and break a lion's jaw with a powerful, well-placed kick. Their feistiness spills over into displays of low-level aggression in the herd with both sexes frequently baring their teeth and nipping. At a waterhole, zebras kick backward at any animal that walks close behind them, even a foal.

Aggressiveness helps them survive, and it has also kept them from being domesticated. However, for a while in the nineteenth century, tame and docile hybrids were used in teams with mules to pull coaches between a city in Zimbabwe and one in South Africa. These hybrids came from zebra mares and donkey stallions , so they were named zebdonks. More recently wild zebdonks that were produced by free-ranging donkeys and zebras in cattle-raising areas of Zimbabwe grazed alongside the donkeys and the cattle. But not for long. Whenever the cattle were herded to a tick dip, the zebdonks panicked and stampeded off, followed by the cattle and then by the angry ranchers.

Kudus, tall antelopes skilled in illusion,
Keep close to thick cover and vanish when they freeze.
Thin stripes down their sides become sunlight through brush,
And the males' spiral horns turn to branches of trees.

174

Antelope horns, curved, straight or spiral in shape, are made of solid bone with an outer covering of the protein material keratin. They're never branched or shed as solid-bone antlers are, and they don't regenerate if they're broken off. Greater kudus *(Tragelaphus strepsiceros)* are among the nine species of antelopes that have spiral horns. Two others are the nyalas of southeastern Africa *(T. angasii)* and the smaller, lesser kudu *(T. imberbis)* of East Africa and the Horn of Africa.

Spiral horns are useful to nyala and kudu males for a better grip in horn-pressing contests. When one of these animals prepares to show his dominance over another male or to impress females, he first makes a lateral body display and proudly presents his horns. Then to demonstrate his martial skills, he furiously attacks vegetation. Often the display is enough to prevent a fight, but if an evenly matched opponent wants to go on with it, the two press horns. Whichever can push the other backward or twist him off balance is the winner, and the loser generally runs off before he is seriously injured. Highly aggressive fights are rare because fatalities can occur from stab wounds, and greater kudu combatants can perish if their long (1.8 m) corkscrew horns become permanently interlocked.

Greater kudus also use their horns to twist and pull down appetizing vines and small branches with new leaves. Because of their long legs and neck, they can browse among trees at heights exceeded only by giraffes and elephants. In addition to their natural diet, they develop a taste for grain crops, and fences don't always keep them from grazing on the delicacies. From a standstill they can jump over a 2.5 m fence, and they have been known to clear 3.5 m when chased or threatened. In southern Africa they also leap across roads at night, creating a hazard to motorists as well as themselves. These habits naturally make them unwelcome in farming areas, and they are frequently shot. Yet due to their shy and secretive behavior, greater kudus have survived in rural areas where other large herbivores have been eradicated.

Like most spiral-horned antelopes, greater and lesser kudus have vertical stripes on their back and patches of white on their face like sun-dappled brush. The males and females of both species have distinctively large ears, pink on the inside with fringes of white hair on the notches and tips. The body color of greater kudu males is pale reddish or grayish brown, but their necks, with a chin-to-chest fringe of beard, are gray, similar to the color of tree trunks. Even in full view at the edge of woodlands, they are inconspicuous when they stand perfectly still, and in dense brush they are almost invisible.

When predators approach and smell or see them through their camouflage, greater kudus give the loudest warning call of any antelope, a harsh *bogh*, and then flee. Graceful jumpers, both sexes are heavy and somewhat clumsy runners, but the males are handicapped by their horns. To avoid being snared by low branches, they have to keep their noses pointing forward as they run so that their horns lie back against their shoulders.

Both greater and lesser kudus are gregarious, though their herds are usually small, from two to four adult females with offspring. Males stay in bachelor herds except during the mating season. Once in Zambia a young male greater kudu that had become orphaned or separated from his mother attached himself to a herd of female impalas for companionship. He remained with them for some time after he was full grown, looking very overgrown by comparison, but apparently presenting no problem to them or the territorial male impala, although he was four times bigger.

Rhinoceros wears her two horns on her snout,
Not true horns, not well matched, but desired by some men.
For her they're stout weapons though lighter than bone:
Like her nails and hairs Rhino's horns grow from her skin.

About 25 million years ago the family Rhinocerotidae was numerous and widespread over the earth. Today only five species are left and all are in danger of extinction. Remnants of three species survive in Asia and two in Africa: the black or hook-lipped rhinoceros *(Diceros bicornis)* and the larger white or square-lipped rhinoceros *(Ceratotherium simum)*. Both African rhino populations now live mainly in southern Africa. A very few individuals of a white rhino subspecies *(C. s. cottoni)* hang on in Garamba Park in Congo, and small groups of black rhinos live in some heavily guarded parks and private reserves in East Africa.

The two species evolved from a common ancestor about eight million years ago. The white rhinoceros developed specialized features for grazing, particularly a wide, square mouth. (The word *white,* or *wit* in Afrikaans *[witrenoster]*, was originally applied to distinguish it from the black rhinoceros, although both are exactly the same slate-gray color. The word *wyd,* or *wide,* is the more accurate description of the wide-lipped, nonwhite animal, but it still goes by its old familiar name, white rhino.)

In order to raise and lower its heavier head, the white rhino also evolved a network of tendons and muscles that are clustered in a prominent hump at the top of its neck. The longer-necked black rhino remained a browser, whose pointed upper or "hooked" lip can reach selectively for leaves. Except in the rainy season under frequent showers, the rhinos look the color of the mud they wallow in to cool down and to get rid of ticks when the mud cakes off.

Although natural forces brought about the gradual disappearance of the other rhinoceroses over their long history, modern man was the cause of their decline into almost total extinction in the last 30 years of the twentieth century, when 99 percent of black rhinos were exterminated. Until then rhinos were killed for their skin and meat; then they were slaughtered for their horns. Shaved or ground horn is still believed by people in the Far East to have medicinal value, and some think it enhances their sexual vigor. In Yemen, northeast of Africa, rhino horns have been fashioned into ornate, status-symbol dagger handles.

But the fantastical horns are made of nothing more magical or potent than ordinary keratin, one of nature's most common building materials. Composed of dense, hairlike filaments but lacking the bony core of antelope horns, they grow from the rhino's skin and continue growing for life.

Both sexes are horned, and the horns are sharp and solid enough to kill other large animals. They are set vertically on the rhino's snout on a strong base that transfers the shocks and stresses of combat or defense to the skull and forequarters. The lower horn is typically longer in white rhinos and is used as a club by males in low-level aggressive encounters with other males. Stabbing is done mainly in defense against lions and hyenas when they make infrequent and usually unsuccessful attempts to snatch young rhinos. Mothers fiercely defend their babies; one was seen goring to death a lion that tried to take her calf. On rare occasions a male stabs another male to death over mating rights to an estrous female. But generally the territorial male thwarts any suitors and keeps the female exclusively to himself during her fertile period every two to three years.

Rhinos can eat and digest extremely coarse plant material. Black rhinos are especially flexible in their food preferences and are able to utilize plants that other herbivores can't eat. Along with having a life span of 40-50 years and no natural enemies, rhinoceroses were among the most enduring of the earth's large mammals until technological man appeared. Yet with recent protection instead of destruction by humans, the white rhinos in southern Africa are no longer on the critically endangered list.

The Ungulates—grazers and browsers, four-hoofed—
Are an awesome assortment: kob, hyrax, impala,
Rhinoceros, duiker, roan, wildebeest, springbok,
Giraffe, aardvark, elephant, warthog, nyala . . .

An animal's skull, teeth and ultimately its DNA reveal its origins and relationships. Its feet provide useful categories for classification. If it has hooves, the horny coverings that protect the front or enclose the ends of its toes, it is an ungulate. Hooves are adaptations for running, and most ungulates are plant-eating herbivores that run to escape danger.

Ungulates, living and extinct, are divided into two major orders on the simple basis of the number of toes inside each hoof. Odd-toed ungulates like zebras with one toe per foot and rhinoceroses with three are in the order Perissodactyla. Ungulates with an even number of toes like antelopes with two per foot and hippopotamuses with four are in the order Artiodactyla. Also considered ungulates because of similarities in their fossil records are four orders of distantly related "near" ungulates: hyraxes (Hyracoidea, "shrew mouse"), elephants (Proboscidea, "proboscis", or trunk), and sea cows (Sirenia, "siren"). Alone in its order Tubulidentata ("tube teeth") is the very distantly related aardvark.

Also called antbear, the aardvark is a powerful digger with muscular limbs, a long snout, and toes ending in thick nails, which may be intermediate between hooves and claws. Not only is it an insectivore, feeding almost entirely on ants and termites, but in outward appearance it is unlike any living ungulate. Its skeleton, however, has many features in common with a proto-ungulate fossil, indicating that its ancient origins were close to those of modern ungulates.

The "near" ungulates also have similarities that point back to early common origins, though their differences are more conspicuous. The several species of hyraxes look like oversize, tailless rodents and are most commonly seen among rocks. Elephants, the largest land animals, and air-breathing but aquatic sea cows, the modern manatees and dugongs, are descended from related ancient ancestors that lived in swamps.

The animals in these three orders share similar features such as teats between the forelegs (female sea cows gave rise to the myth of mermaids), internal testes and the same type of uterus. Elephants and hyraxes both have relatively unmodified limbs with between two and five toes covered by nails instead of hooves. Manatees and dugongs have five joined digits inside their front flippers. Before 65 million years ago, the very ancient ancestors of these near ungulates, which probably originated in Africa, had even more ancient common ancestry with perissodactyls.

The perissodactyls include single-toed horses, asses and zebras, and three-toed rhinoceroses. They are nonruminants—they don't chew cud—and they were the most abundant herbivores between 55 and 25 million years ago. Today these few remaining species are far outnumbered by the even-toed artiodactyls.

Most artiodactyls have horns and most are ruminants: their digestive system is adapted for eating plants with hard-to-digest cellulose, which is turned by fermentation into digestible carbohydrates. Ruminating, or chewing cud, is one step in the hours- or days-long digestion process. Cud is lumps of coarse pieces of plant material that have been chewed briefly, swallowed into the rumen, the largest of the four chambers of the stomach, and then regurgitated a mouthful at a time to be rechewed. The second chewing breaks down the plant particles into finer pieces with more surfaces. When they're swallowed again, symbiotic microorganisms in the rumen ferment the cellulose, splitting it into simpler compounds for gastric digestion.

Animals that don't chew cud, the nonruminants, quickly eat and excrete their fibrous, often low-quality food, and they process it inefficiently. Some fermentation takes place in the cecum, a bacteria-filled pouch between the small and large intestines, but much of the fiber is not digested, as their coarser dung indicates. Among domestic livestock, nonruminants are horses, donkeys and pigs. Wild nonruminants include zebras, elephants, hippos, warthogs and all wild pigs.

Cud-chewing ruminants obtain nutrients by thoroughly processing their plant food, and their dead microorganisms absorbed with it give them animal protein as well. With less efficient processing of less nutritious food, nonruminants have to work harder and longer at eating to be well nourished. Lying around contentedly chewing cud like a goat or a gazelle is a ruminant luxury.

Quagga is gone, extinct more than a century,
Stock overgrazing helped hasten the kill.
A zebra subspecies—striped upper parts only—
Today's zebras echo its *kwah-ha* call still.

An 1864 photograph of a female quagga that lived in the Gardens of the Zoological Society of London from 1851 to 1872. Photo: Zoological Society of London.

The Hottentot word *quagga*, pronounced *KWAH-ha*, mimics the distance call of plains, or Burchell's, zebras and their extinct relatives, which were named for the sound. The last living quagga *(Equus quagga)* died in the Amsterdam Zoo in late summer 1883. By then quaggas had already disappeared from their home in the Karoo, the vast semidesert plateau in southwest South Africa. Only a few decades earlier immense herds were still being seen in one area, but by about 1880 they were gone.

Several photographs of a quagga exist along with a detailed old oil painting. In the South African Museum there is a stuffed quagga foal, and about 20 other specimens are in various international museums. The depicted animals and some of the specimens look like zebras except for the distinctive coloring. Whereas zebras have black stripes on a white body, quaggas have pale, yellowish brown stripes on a reddish brown body with a dark band down their back. On both the mounted specimens and the animal in the photographs, the stripes grow faint around their sides, then become irregular spots and finally fade completely at their white rump. Their belly, tail and legs are also white. The brown coloring could have been an adaptation to make them less conspicuous on the dusty flat landscape of the Karoo. The white on their lower body was probably an adaptation to reflect heat from the ground.

Quaggas lived in the right place at the wrong time. In 1885 legislation was passed to protect them, but by then they had all died naturally or been killed. They were major competitors of livestock in a dry habitat where the vegetation can support only limited numbers of herbivores, and conservation was not ordinarily practiced. In 1822 near the western edge of the Karoo, the veld, or natural grassland, was reported to have been so heavily grazed by sheep that hardly a blade of grass remained. The hungry sheep and other grazers may have stripped the fragile land so that quaggas weren't left with enough to eat.

Not only were they considered a threat to livestock, they were also hunted for their hides and meat and for sport. The plains zebras must have been hunted as well—the two groups of animals were both referred to as quaggas in the nineteenth century—but the smaller population of quaggas was more vulnerable, and they disappeared before anyone realized how endangered they were.

Although the original animals are extinct, twentieth and twenty-first century technology might be able to re-create them as virtual originals. In the process of remounting the quagga foal and then two other specimens in German museums in 1980, the chief taxidermist for the South African Museum collected and preserved blood and tissue fragments. Some of these were later sent to a research zoologist, who extracted DNA from the fragments and obtained pieces of the gene. The analysis determined that quaggas were a subspecies of plains zebras and that their genes still exist in modern populations. Unlike the fiction of dinosaur re-creation from genetic material of long-dead animals, the actual creation of replicas of quaggas from genes in living animals might be possible.

For a rebreeding program, specific zebras were selected with the most pronounced quaggalike characteristics. So far the stripes of the foals have been diminished, and some have been born with completely unstriped hindquarters. But the brown color has not yet appeared, and this and other problems suggest to some people that the quagga was a separate species of zebra rather than a subspecies, or that it was simply a color variation of Burchell's zebras. Or perhaps the creation of a virtual quagga requires twenty-second century technology.

By some lights brown Tsetse Flies look eco-green:
When they jab flesh for blood, they pass on dreaded parasites
Harmless to wildlife but fatal to livestock:
Wild places stay wild under tsetse air strikes.

190

Tsetse flies *(genus Glossina)* are infamous in sub-Saharan Africa for carrying two deadly diseases: sleeping sickness in humans and nagana, a similar disease in livestock. Each is caused by a particular type of trypanosome, a single-celled parasite that is transmitted through a fly's saliva when it bites and sucks blood from a host animal.

A fly is not born infected. It acquires a dose of trypanosomes only by having a meal of blood from a host that carries them, as many wild animals do. Over millions of years African wildlife has developed immunity to nagana, but relatively recent domestic arrivals have not, so they succumb. Humans have never acquired immunity either, although they cannot be infected with nagana, only with sleeping sickness from a fly that has bitten another person.

Animals don't get sleeping sickness, but in one case a wild animal developed nagana. A pet warthog had been raised on a bottle and lacked the immune system defenses her mother's milk would have given her. She was easily cured with drugs, which are effective for both forms of the disease if administered early enough, but which have an impossibly high cost for subsistence-level farmers.

Tsetse flies belong to the order Diptera, which is one of six orders with insects that feed on blood. Tsetses, both males and females, never meet a vertebrate animal whose blood they don't like. They suck it from monitor lizards and snakes as well as elephants and ostriches, and they readily bite humans, but human blood is not among their favorites. (In the wild they prefer warthog and bushpig blood.) After mating, a female tsetse may be even less selective because she needs large amounts of blood (for a fly) to nourish her single larva.

The larva hatches inside her uterus and feeds from a "milk gland" for about two weeks. Then she deposits it, as a fully grown larva, in moist, shady soil for its next development stage as a pupa, and after a month it hatches as an adult. In comparison with most insects, which have great numbers of offspring, tsetse flies along with dung beetles produce very few larvae—around 10—during their short (six-month) reproductive lifetime. While the low birth rate means far fewer tsetses, each developing larva receives prime protein nourishment and protection within the mother and thus begins life in the outside world with a good chance of survival.

When research was going on to try to eradicate tsetse flies from agricultural areas (they have been wiped out of South Africa), the most desirable attractant was found to be cow's breath, which was collected from cattle in underground holding areas or in caves. Now the odor is produced artificially and used as bait along with visually stimulating bright blue and black sheets. The traps are an eyesore in a natural setting, but they decrease tsetse annoyance to income-producing tourists and legal hunters.

If tsetse flies were eliminated from the continent, as many people would like, human deaths from sleeping sickness would cease. Even though most flies do not carry the parasites, their stinging, red-hot needle bites and itching welts would no longer have to be endured. Nagana would disappear and livestock would be grazed in what is now tsetse-controlled bush. More and more wild habitats would be destroyed as trees were cut down and the land cultivated. Then, illegally but inevitably, livestock would also be grazed in the lush grass and vegetation of parks and protected areas. And slowly but certainly the wildlife would be eliminated.

MISLEADING FIRST IMPRESSIONS
AND FLEETING LAST ONES

Giraffe walks on stilt legs as tall as a thorn tree,
His stubby horns wrapped in skin, eyes fringed in lashes.
Despite his soft looks, he can land a mean kick,
And his walloping neck swing wins dominance clashes.

T here is always something new out of Africa", wrote the Roman scholar Pliny the Elder in his *Natural History*, and when incredulous people first looked at a giraffe *(Giraffa camelopardalis)*, some thought they were beholding an African cross between a leopard and a camel. The creature had a leopard's spotted coat, a face somewhat like a camel's and the slow, ambling gait of a camel.

In natural history in the modern world, herbivores don't mate with carnivores, and even if they did, logistics would probably keep camels from mating with leopards. (Nor can camels produce offspring from mating with giraffes, as the two species are unrelated.) The sole living relatives of giraffes are okapis *(Okapia johnstoni)*, the dark brown herbivores with horizontal, flame-shaped white stripes on their legs and rump. Timid and rarely seen (okapis were not known to scientists until the early 1900s), okapis live in the forests of Congo under threat from civil conflict; the vast, illegal bushmeat trade; and the increasing penetration of their habitat by loggers.

The world's tallest animals, male giraffes can grow to 5.5 m and females to 4.5 m, and they browse in trees at heights only elephants can reach with their trunk. Their very flexible lips and long (45-cm) tongue pluck out the most nutritious top leaves, particularly from thorny acacia trees, and hard papillae, or nipplelike protuberances, protect their tongue and lips from the thorns. Papillae also line their stomach and give it the greatest absorptive area of any ruminant's. With such efficient digestion and high-quality browse, giraffes stay well nourished with less food than most other ruminants.

In their leisurely browsing they look as if they're daydreaming. Their big, thick-lashed eyes are wide set in prominent sockets, and they gaze down on the world with a mild, slightly sleepy expression. But that belies their constant alertness. Both their night vision and their day vision are acute, and from so high a vantage point, they clearly see distant predators.

If danger is close, giraffes can gallop off at nearly 60 kph, appearing to run in slow motion because of their long legs and relatively short trunk. Although young giraffes can sprint faster than adults, when separated from their mother they are frequent victims of lions and hyenas. A female defends her offspring by kicking with her fore- and hind feet as males do, and both sexes put enough force behind their heavy hooves to kill any predator.

For a fight between themselves, two male giraffes use different but almost as damaging weapons—their long muscular neck and their thick-boned, knobby-horned head. Their stubby horns, present in the embryo, begin as unattached cartilage and are later overlain with deposits of bone and fused to the skull. They are covered by skin and surrounded by thin fringes of hair in young animals and females but are bald in mature males. Bone continues to be deposited on the horns and over the entire skull of males except where muscles are attached. It accumulates in lumpy deposits over the eyes, on the nose and at the base of the skull so that the older a bull grows, the heavier and more clublike his head becomes.

A duel begins with the two bulls standing close together with their legs apart to brace themselves. First one and then the other swings his neck up and back trying to strike with his horns. But the opponent moves slightly away to avoid the brunt of the blow and to position his neck to strike back. Because each one rides the blows, the combatants ordinarily don't cause severe injury. One of them, typically a stranger in the territory, retreats after a few hits. Local males learn their place in the loosely organized giraffe society by "necking" in mock combat when they're young.

Duck-faced and flat-headed, Ostrich looks daffy,
But he's not daft enough to stand head in the ground.
He runs fast, kicks hard with his two-toed clawed feet
And for night-stalkers turns on his lion-roar sound.

Viewing ostriches (*Struthio camelus*) at a distance, early desert travelers thought they looked like camels (thus their scientific name, which means "sparrow camel"). More fanciful observers thought they saw ostriches bury their head to avoid facing danger, and the myth is still believed. But the illusion is easily explained as simple cause and effect in one or a combination of two common behaviors. When ostriches eat short grass and plants, they lower their long neck without bending their long legs, and their head disappears from view. And when a female brooding eggs sees a predator approaching, she stretches flat on the ground. The mound of her brown-feathered body is camouflaged as a dusty bush, and her head and neck are out of sight—but still above ground.

Ostriches never bury their head, and adults don't hide from danger (chicks do). They run from it, sprinting at 70 kph and maintaining speeds up to 50 kph for nearly half an hour, with their clusters of soft, drooping feathers bouncing behind like a bustle. When they can't escape an attack, they fight back with a powerful kick and the sharp claw on the larger of their two toes. Territorial males are especially aggressive when they sit on their shallow scrape of a nest at night, and they have killed people trying to steal their huge, 1.5 kg eggs (each the equivalent of two dozen hen's eggs).

To be less conspicuous for the night shift as well as more conspicuous for daylight mating displays, they have mainly black feathers with white wings and a gray or brown tail. The females wear drab grayish brown and beige for their daytime brooding. Males also use a feature from their mating display as another kind of camouflage—a deep booming call that sounds like the roar of a lion. Lions can probably tell the difference, but other predators such as leopards, wild dogs and cheetahs may be put off. Along with the big sound, males perform elaborate bowing and wing flapping to impress the females.

A territorial male has a harem that includes a major hen and several minor hens. The hens all lay eggs in the same nest, but only the male and the major hen do the brooding. Each hen lays three to eight eggs, depending on her age and rank, and she lays one egg every other afternoon. Amid all the comings and goings, the male guards the eggs until the clutch of up to 25 is complete. When the laying is finished, several eggs lie apart from the main group. These are not a surplus that didn't fit in the nest but a buffer. Able to identify her own eggs, the major hen pushes aside some of the minor hens' eggs for predators to take instead of hers.

Despite living so close, the sharp-eyed Bushmen didn't realize that ostriches, at least the females, aren't as foolish as they look. In one of their folktales the Creator instructed His assistant to give fire to Man. But the assistant feared that Man would use it unwisely, so he gave it to Ostrich to guard. Any creature who could get the fire away from the strong and protective bird would be wise enough to use it well.

Ostrich put the fire under his wing, but First Bushman discovered the hiding place and devised a plan. He told Ostrich that he had dreamed the bird would be able to fly if he stood on a high hill before dawn with his eyes closed and his wings outstretched. Ostrich wanted to fly so badly that he forgot his duty and followed the instructions, and First Bushman grabbed the fire. The bird was so upset at not becoming able to fly as well as losing the fire entrusted to him that he became dotty. To this day he must leave some of the eggs outside the nest to remind himself of what he should be doing.

Comical Warthog is flat-out courageous
To snooze near hyenas, send leopards up trees.
He backs in his burrow, tusks aimed at attackers,
He runs with his tail up and eats on his knees.

Of the two warthog species, common warthogs *(Phacochoerus africanus)* are still abundant on savannas and open woodlands and in many national parks. But they have been eradicated from heavily farmed areas because of their crop raiding and because they carry diseases that infect livestock. The other species *(P. aethiopicus)* lives in the dry scrubland of northern Kenya and Somalia. Its much smaller population is considered vulnerable by the World Conservation Union (IUCN), partly due to the proliferation of automatic weapons, which threaten all wildlife as well as people.

Except for the desert warthogs' shorter, broader head, the two species look identical. Both have a black or reddish brown erectile crest that lies limp over their shoulders when they're relaxed and a line of white whiskers on their lower cheeks. On baby warthogs the whiskers look like little tusks. The tusks in mature males are their sharp upper canine teeth, which can curve out nearly 60 cm from their long, flat face. They also have a pair of lower tusks that are smaller but are constantly honed to razor sharpness against the upper canines.

Their hallmark features, their "warts", are actually growths of gristle and thickened skin. A large pair extends about 15 cm from under the eyes of males, and a smaller pair sprouts near their tusks. All four warts may help protect their eyes from an opponent's tusks in their sometimes fatal pushing and striking fights, and both the warts and tusks keep the combatants going head-to-head during a duel. Females have one pair of warts and much smaller but still dangerous tusks.

Since warthogs' gray skin is almost hairless and there's little fat beneath it, they have to work at thermoregulation. Sudden temperature changes can kill piglets, but adults have ways of coping with extremes. For warmth they lie in the sun, huddled together if possible, or they go into one of several abandoned aardvark burrows that they occupy on a first-come, first-served basis with other warthogs and an occasional time-sharing hyena. On a cold, rainy day they may not come out at all. In hot weather they wallow in mud and stretch out in whatever shade they can find, even if it's under the same tree as a drowsy hyena.

Cartoonish and comical in appearance, warthogs have behaviors to match. Trotting through tall grass or across an open area, both adults and piglets hold their black-tufted tail straight up. The "flag" isn't necessarily a warning of danger or a contact signal to other warthogs but a display of alertness. Under stress they raise the crest of hair on their back. When they're chased by a predator, they race for a nearby burrow, counting on it to be unoccupied, especially by a hyena or a porcupine. At the last second they whirl around and push in backwards so that the pursuer is confronted by sharp tusks instead of a plump rump. Piglets that outrun the predator plunge in headfirst.

Because their neck is short and thick, adult warthogs can't bend to graze, so in behavior unique among pigs they kneel on heavy calluses with their back legs straight. They also "walk" bottoms up on their padded knees when they move from one patch of grass to another nearby. In the dry season they dig for nutritious roots and stems with their hard nasal disk, and they sometimes eat carrion. If they encounter a rat or snake in their foraging, they will kill and eat it. Once a mother and her offspring stopped grazing to kneel around a Cape buffalo skull and nibble on it for its minerals.

Mothers aggressively and courageously try to defend their young, and several times they have been seen driving off single cheetahs and leopards. But despite their valiant efforts, in the first six months mortality among piglets can be over 60 percent. Against lions, even a large male warthog is usually doomed since the cats will dig a warthog out of its burrow or wait for it to emerge in the morning. Hyenas snatch piglets when they can, but they generally leave adults and their tusks alone. Once on a hot afternoon in Botswana two male warthogs nonchalantly came to wallow in the cool mud at one side of a shrinking waterhole, just a few meters away from two hyenas that were lolling at the other end.

Called Aardwolf, he's really a timid hyena,
Who raises his hackles and roars a fierce bluff.
His teeth are too weak to crack bones or chew meat,
So it's ground-swarming termites he hunts and laps up.

S hy, nocturnal and seldom seen, the aardwolf *(Proteles cristatus)*, Afrikaans for "earth wolf", lives in the earth in one of several burrows and has long, thick fur. But it's unrelated to wolves or any canids. This mammal is a hyena, as the first settlers in southern Africa might have suspected if they had seen its close resemblance to the striped hyena, which is found in North and East Africa but not in the southern subregion.

The aardwolf has a hairless black muzzle, yellowish brown fur with vertical stripes, and both an erectile neck mane and a shoulders-to-tail crest. When it raises all this fur, its apparent size increases by more than 70 percent. As further reinforcement of the illusion that it's much larger and stronger than its slender build, sloping back and 10 kg of weight add up to, it gives an explosive bark and an unexpectedly loud roar. If the startling display doesn't intimidate a predator, the aardwolf's only other defense is to race for its burrow using its bushy tail as a rudder and a bite-deflecting shield.

Both sexes defend their offspring against jackals, and in the breeding season males fight each other with their long, sharp but thin canine teeth. Their teeth give them away. Although their canines and incisors are normally developed, their cheek teeth (the molars and premolars) are almost useless pegs, far too weak and small to crack bones or chew tough flesh as their hyena relatives do. But their food needs little or no chewing, and a flow of thick, sticky saliva makes it easy to swallow. The food is harvester termites almost exclusively. Aardwolves are carnivores turned insectivores.

The nocturnal species of termites they prefer can be heard from several meters away cutting dry grass above ground for their underground nest, so aardwolves find them by walking slowly and listening. If it starts to rain, they stop foraging, since the sound of raindrops masks the rustling of the termites. When they locate a swarm, their wide tongue moves as fast as a cat's lapping water to lick up hundreds of workers before they rush back underground and before too many soldiers rush up. In a night's foraging one aardwolf laps up 200,000 or more termites. This protein-rich meal weighs about a kilo and provides the equivalent nutritional value of $^3/_4$ kg of lean meat.

But each course has a price: soldier termites quickly line up to cover the retreating workers by squirting threads of turpentine-like chemicals, and aardwolves can't avoid lapping up quantities of the soldiers before moving on to a more appetizing, undefended swarm. The workers taste good, so getting the soldiers with them is an acceptable trade-off, and aardwolves can tolerate the poison. Their digestive system is specialized for handling substantial amounts of it, just as their larger meat-eating relatives can digest putrid flesh without harm.

They also take in sandy soil and pieces of cut grass as they eat, and their droppings are consequently very large, numerous and strong smelling. They defecate into a narrow trench they dig in one of their territory's several latrines and then scrape soil on top of the dung. This helps cover the pungent odor that could interfere with their smelling of scent marks, and it prevents contamination of the food patches. Like other hyenas, they mark their territory by extruding their anal pouch and pasting a lingering, sweet-smelling secretion on stems and stalks near latrines and dens. They leave fainter scent marks wherever they have foraged to indicate to themselves and to their mate and offspring that the food supply is temporarily low.

Because they're so dependent on just one food that becomes scarce in the winter months, aardwolves often go through long periods of weight loss and being in poor condition. They can survive difficult natural circumstances, including the toxic chemicals from their food, but they have little chance against humans. They're frequently killed by domestic dogs in rural communities, and they're hunted for their fur. Throughout their range in East and southern Africa, they're destroyed on roads at night because they become dazzled and paralyzed by vehicle headlights.

Only slightly like hares, bright-eyed Springhares are rodents:
The way that they gnaw and chew plants is the clue.
With their powerful hind legs and long tail for balance,
The way that they hop, they're like small kangaroos.

S ince springhares *(Pedetes capensis)* don't leave their burrows to forage until long after sundown, early observers trying to make them out across dark fields thought they looked like hares. But springhares are rodents and unrelated to hares, although they resemble them more than rats or the other two major rodent forms, squirrels and porcupines. These "jumping rats" are so different from their modern rodent relatives that they are the sole members of their own Pedetidae family. They probably share ancient common ancestry with anomalures, African flying squirrels.

Their superficial similarities to hares (e.g., *Lepus saxatilis*) are their size (3 kg), shape and soft-textured fur. Their differences are their long, black-tipped brush of a tail; much shorter ears; curved claws on their tiny forelegs, which they fold under their chin when they're not digging or holding food; and powerful, muscular hind legs, also clawed. Hares run; springhares hop like miniature kangaroos, making leaps of 3–4 m at speeds of nearly 25 kph when they're being chased.

Several internal features define them as rodents rather than hares, particularly their teeth. Their two pairs of sharp, curved incisors keep growing, and springhares have to keep gnawing so they'll stay short, functional and safely away from their throat and jaws. Because the teeth are enameled on the outside only, the less durable inner surface wears down and they become chisel shaped. They're constantly honed against each other as the animals gnaw, and the razor edges allow springhares to bite through hard plant material. As they gnaw, their lower jaw moves forward so their cheek teeth can't meet and wear out by abrasion. When they chew, the lower jaw moves back and the cheek teeth come together.

Springhares' natural diet is almost entirely the wild grasses that grow in the compacted sandy soil of their habitat, and they eat all parts of the plants from roots to seeds. But they easily acquire a taste for cultivated crops such as maize and groundnuts. In some semiarid farming areas they have become pests, and small populations have been eradicated. They're considered very tasty by rural people in various parts of southern Africa and also by many mammalian carnivores as well as pythons and eagle owls. Yet springhares are not endangered overall, despite the high predation and their relatively low birth rate.

Females give birth to only one baby at a time though they may have three to four in a year. A youngster remains in its mother's burrow until it's several weeks old and half the size of an adult, and when it emerges, it can move almost as quickly as an adult. While springhares' main defense is their fast, long leaps, they use their hind claws to rake an attacker, and they also bite if they're captured. When they're pursued, they dash into their burrow and rapidly block the several entrances and the escape hole to prevent a small predator from following them in. Each burrow is occupied by only one springhare, and it may extend with twists and turns for more than 40 m.

At night in a beam of light across a field, the large, reflective eyes of springhares look like single candles bouncing and floating over the ground. Curiously, only one eye on each animal shows in the light. When the beam is directed straight at them close by, they stop transfixed and bob their head as they stare into it. One night the headlights of a vehicle caught and held two springhares in the middle of a road. They were scavenging at a road kill, just as any opportunistic rat might do.

Though tail-wagging Thomson's Gazelles, nicknamed tommies,
Seem easy prey pickings in wide-open spaces,
Their strong lines of defense are vigilance, keen sight
And sudden sharp turns to escape from tight chases.

216

Gazelles are a successful group of antelopes that range from Siberia to South Africa. On the savannas of East Africa they are represented by Thomson's gazelles *(Gazella thomsonii)*, or "tommies", and by the larger, lighter-colored Grant's gazelles *(G. granti)*. In southwest Africa springboks *(Antidorcas marsupialis)* live in similar semidesert habitats and closely resemble tommies, but they're related only distantly.

Visual signals are important to Thomson's gazelles, as they are to all gazelles. Tommies constantly flick their short black tail across their white rear, and they twitch their conspicuous black side stripe just as they bolt from danger. Their most obvious danger signal is stotting—bounding with their back and legs straight and their tail raised. (Springboks *pronk* even more elaborately, curving their body and flaring a strip of white fur, which is normally concealed in a scented skin pouch on their back.) This action also indicates excitement or exuberance among calves, and the stotting of young calves signals their mothers that they have been flushed from hiding. When predators are wild dogs or hyenas hunting in a pack, stotting gazelles create a ripple of motion that is a clear warning to scattered herd members even if the hunters aren't yet visible.

Their other danger signal, common to many plains animals, is a cautious approach to a suspicious object they can't identify. They approach a passing predator as well, gathering at a safe flight distance to watch and frequently to follow it. When it stops, some of the tommies walk around in a small circle, still staring at it intently. Not only do they let the predator know it can't make a surprise attack, but they also let distant herd members see by their actions that trouble may be on the way.

At over 80 kph, a Thomson's gazelle can outrun any predator except a cheetah, which can overtake it in a straight sprint but becomes too exhausted to catch it if the tommy is able to make a few sharp turns. Wild dogs are almost impossible to escape because of their numbers and greater stamina. Tommies are a staple food for them and for cheetahs, and their calves are taken by jackals. Despite the high predation, however, their herds of thousands prove how resilient they are. Like adaptable impalas, which also live in the same savanna habitat, tommies graze on grass when it's green, and when it dries up, they browse on plants, migrating back and forth from the eastern plains to tall grasslands and open woodlands for the dry season.

Tommy females, which have a new calf every six to seven months, contribute to the success of their species by their cooperative defense of young, a behavior they share with Grant's and other gazelles but not with other antelopes. Like most baby antelopes, a baby tommy is a "hider", either taking cover under plants or lying flat on the ground for about two weeks after birth. Because its scent glands don't function during this time and because it lies motionless unless a predator is very close, it is easily overlooked. The mother forages nearby and returns to suckle the calf and consume its wastes, which her licking stimulates it to eliminate.

If a jackal happens to discover a calf, the mother and one or more tommy females quickly come to defend it. Since jackals generally hunt in pairs, the assistant tries to drive the second jackal off while the mother and another female stand with their heads lowered between the calf and the first jackal. Sometimes their aggression, mild though it is, is enough to send the predators looking for less plucky prey. Attitude is what does it. The horns of female Thomson's gazelles are typically short and thin, or broken or absent altogether.

With speed to spare Cheetah, least catlike of cats,
Sprints a 100-plus kph after gazelle.
He bands with his brothers—the females are loners—
And hunts in the sun on savanna and veld.

220

Cats are the most specialized of carnivores, and cheetahs *(Acinonyx jubatus)* are the most specialized of cats. Their large nasal passages, lungs and heart give them maximum intake and distribution of oxygen during and after a chase, and chasing is what they do best.

Where other cats have skeletons adapted for climbing and leaping, cheetahs' skeletons and internal organs are adapted for running. They have a long thin body, long powerful hind legs and a flexible spinal column that lets them take strides of almost 9 m and hit speeds over 100 kph for short bursts. Their blunt claws, which are partially retractable although not covered by a sheath, give them purchase on hard ground, and the tire-tread ridges on their forepaws help prevent skidding.

In ancient times, according to a Bushman folktale, Cheetah had soft, catlike paws, but he could still run very fast. One day the Creator held a race to see who was faster, Cheetah or Tsessebe, one of the swiftest antelopes. Cheetah knew that his soft paws were not suited for defeating that fleet opponent, so he borrowed hard paws from an agreeable wild dog. During the race Tsessebe broke his leg, and Cheetah stopped to help him instead of running ahead to win. For his kindness the Creator allowed Cheetah to keep the hard paws, and He made him the fastest animal in the land.

Cheetahs are faster than any animal but only for about 300 m. If they don't catch their quarry within that distance, they must give up and cool down before trying again. They hunt mainly medium-size antelopes, ignoring those that stand their ground, such as territorial males, since they need the prey's momentum to bring it down. When they're close enough, they slap the animal's shoulder or rump with their forepaw, securing a hold with their sharp dewclaw and throwing it off balance. Otherwise they trip it. They kill by suffocation, which may take as long as 20 minutes, and their jaws are adapted for clamping on the throat. Their nose is set higher than most carnivores' on their relatively short muzzle so that they can continue panting as they maintain their grip.

While cheetahs are most evident on open grassland, they commonly occur in lightly wooded or scrub-covered habitats. More important to them than the vegetation are abundant prey and relatively little competition. They hunt almost entirely in daylight in order to minimize the chances of their kills being stolen by night-hunting lions and hyenas, which nonetheless take about 10 percent.

Their defensive display is a widemouthed snarl that extends their black "tear marks" into a circle with their black lips and, enhanced by their white facial fur, gives the illusion of larger jaws and teeth. They also hiss, growl and slap the ground with their forepaws, but they don't fight to defend their kill. Less muscular, with smaller teeth and blunter claws, these cats are more timid than other predators. A single cheetah, especially a female, always retreats, but a coalition of two or more aggressive males sometimes intimidates the scavengers into backing off.

Successful hunts average about 40 percent, somewhat higher for a female with cubs because she is more careful in selecting prey that she can bring down without harming herself in the process. Like domestic cats, a mother captures live young animals for the cubs to practice treating as prey and not as playthings. Killing is learned behavior, and although the cubs stalk and pull down small mammals when they're 12 months old, they typically don't kill them until they're older.

Cubs stay with the mother until they're between 16 and 22 months old and then leave as a group. While the brothers tend to remain together, young females separate to live and raise their cubs alone. Shortly after, the mother goes searching for a desirable new mate. One reason for the failure of past captive breeding programs is that the breeders selected males they thought were desirable and then kept them near the females. They finally figured out that females want to be left alone to make their own choices in their own good time.

REFERENCES

Books

Alden, Peter C., Richard D. Estes, Duane Schlitter and Bunny McBride. 1995. *National Audubon Society Field Guide to African Wildlife*. New York: Alfred A. Knopf.

Allaby, Michael. 1999. *A Dictionary of Zoology*. Oxford: Oxford University Press.

Apps, P. 1992. *Wild Ways: A Field Guide to the Behaviour of Southern African Mammals*. Johannesburg: Southern Book Publishers (Pty) Ltd.

Carr, Norman. n.d. *Kakuli*. Harare, Zimbabwe: CBC Publishing.

Cillie, B. 1997. *The Mammal Guide of Southern Africa*. Pretoria: Briza Publications.

Comley, Peter, and Salome Meyer. 1997. *A Field Guide to the Mammals of Namibia*. Kasane, Zimbabwe: Africa Window.

Estes, Richard Despard. 1991. *The Behavior Guide to African Mammals*. Los Angeles: The University of California Press.

_____. 1999. *The Safari Companion: A Guide to Watching African Mammals*. 2nd ed., rev. White River Junction, Vermont: Chelsea Green Publishing Company.

Greaves, Nick. 1989. *When Hippo Was Hairy and Other Tales from Africa*. Johannesburg: Southern Book Publishers.

_____. 1993. *When Lion Could Fly and Other Tales from Africa*. Johannesburg: Southern Book Publishers.

Hall-Martin, A. 1997. *Cats of Africa*. Cape Town: Fernwood Press.

Joyce, Peter. 1999. *From Aardvark to Zebra: Secrets of African Wildlife*. Cape Town: Struik Publishers.

Kenmuir, D., and R. Williams. 1975. *Wild Mammals: A Field Guide and Introduction to the Mammals of Zimbabwe*. Harare: Longman Zimbabwe.

Kingdon, Jonathan. 1997. *The Kingdon Field Guide to African Mammals*. London: Academic Press Limited.

Library of the World's Myths and Legends. 1968. *Egyptian Mythology*. New York: Peter Bedrick Books.

Maclean, Gordon Lindsay. 1993. *Roberts' Birds of Southern Africa*. 6th ed. Cape Town: Published by The Trustees of the John Voelcker Bird Book Fund.

McNutt, John, and Lesley Boggs. 1996. *Running Wild*. Johannesburg: Southern Book Publishers.

Newman, Kenneth. 1994. *Birds of Southern Africa*. 4th ed. Johannesburg: Southern Book Publishers.

Patterson, R. 1989. *Snakes*. Cape Town: Struik Publishers

Reader's Digest. 1989. *Southern African Wildlife: A Guide to Our Mammals, Birds, Reptiles, Insects, Fishes, Amphibians, Invertebrates*. Cape Town: The Reader's Digest Association Southern Africa (Pty) Ltd.

Richards, Dave. 1995. *A Photographic Guide to Birds of East Africa*. Sanibel Island, Florida: Ralph Curtis Publishing, Inc.

Skinner, J. D., and R. H. N. Smithers. 1990. *The Mammals of the Southern African Subregion*. 2nd ed. Pretoria: The University of Pretoria.

Smithers, Reay H. N. 1983. *The Mammals of the Southern African Subregion*. Pretoria: The University of Pretoria.

Stuart, Chris, and Tilde Stuart. 1992. *Southern, Central and East African Mammals: A Photographic Guide*. Cape Town: Struik Publishers (Pty) Ltd.

Whellan, J. A. 1967. *The Bundu Book of Birds, Insects and Snakes*. Harare: Longman Zimbabwe.

Articles

Bearder, Simon K. "Calls of the Wild". *Natural History*, August 1995, 48-57.

Beck, Alan. "All About the African Clawed Frog." *Herp Hacienda Library*, July 1996. Available at http://petstation.com/clfrog.html

Berry, Philip. "Friends in High Places". *BBC Wildlife*, July 1994, 18-26.

Brett, Rob. "Romancing the Naked Mole-Rat". *Swara: The Magazine of the East African Wildlife Society*, March/April 1987, 9-11.

Britton, Adam. "Crocodylus Niloticus". 1995. Available at
    http://www.bio.bris.ac.uk/research/bats/csp_cnil.htm

Conniff, Richard. "Africa's Wild Dogs". *National Geographic,* May 1999, 37-63.

Creel, Scott. "Sizing Up the Competition". *Natural History,* September 1998, 34-42.

East, Marion, and Herbert Hofer. "Serengeti Nights". *Wildlife Conservation,* August 1995, 36-45.

"Extra Sensory Perception". *The Economist,* January 6, 2001, 74-75.

Hanel, Christine. "The Misty Desert". *Flamingo: The In-Flight Magazine of Air Namibia,* October
    1996, 8-15.

Klingel, Hans. "Fluctuating Fortunes of the River Horse". *Natural History,* May 1995, 46-56.

"Naked Mole-Rats". *Science News* (Cornell University), July and November 1996. Available at
    http://www.news.cornell.edu/science/July96/molebook.hrs.html and
    http://www.news.cornell.edu/science/Nov96/recruit.hrs.html

Okedi, L.M.A. "Least Specific Sucker of Vertebrate Blood". *University of Florida Book of Insect
    Records,* May 8, 1995. Available at http://gnv.ifas.ufl.edu/~tjw/chap10.htm

Shoshani, Jeheskel. "It's a Nose! It's a Hand! "It's an Elephant's Trunk!" *Natural History,*
    November 1997, 36-45.

Stuller, Jay. "Speed". *Wildlife Conservation,* August 1996, 28-35.

Swart, Jonathan. "To Scale a Pangolin". *Vision of Wildlife, Ecotourism and the Environment in
    Southern Africa,* Fourth Annual 2000, 48-53.

Vergnani, Linda. "What Was, Is About To Be". *Sawubona,* December 1998, 84-89.

Zimmer, Carl. "Prepared for the Past". *Natural History,* April 2001, 28-29.

Measurements Used

Metric	US equivalent
Millimeter (mm)	.04 inch
Centimeter (cm)	.39 inch
Meter (m)	39.37 inches
Kilometer (km)	.62 mile
Hectare (ha)	2.47 acres
Gram (g)	.035 ounce
Kilogram (kg)	2.21 pounds
Liter (l)	1.06 quarts

Temperature

Degrees Centigrade	Degrees Fahrenheit
0	32
30	86
37	98.6
40	104

Classifications, from largest group to smallest

Order

Family

Genus

Species